Piano

Classical
Piano Anthology 4

12 Original Works
Including pieces by Czerny, Mozart and Beethoven

Selected and edited by Nils Franke

ED 13443
ISMN 979-0-2201-3278-0
ISBN 978-1-84761-260-1

www.schott-music.com

Mainz • London • Berlin • Madrid • New York • Paris • Prague • Tokyo • Toronto

Acknowledgements / Remerciements / Danksagung

I am grateful to Mary and David Bowerman whose generous support has enabled the CD to be recorded in the excellent setting of Champs Hill Music Room. A special mention must go to the production team of the CD, Ateş Orga and Ken Blair, for their expertise and contribution to this project.

Je remercie Mary et David Bowerman dont le généreux soutien a permis d'enregistrer le CD dans les excellentes conditions offertes par le Champs Hill Music Room. Il me faut également citer tout particulièrement l'équipe de production du CD, Ateş Orga et Ken Blair, pour leur savoir-faire et leur précieuse contribution à ce projet.

Ich danke Mary und David Bowerman für ihre großzügige Unterstützung, die es ermöglicht hat, die CD im großartigen Ambiente des Champs Hill Music Room aufzunehmen. Ein besonderer Dank geht an das Produktionsteam der CD, Ateş Orga und Ken Blair für ihr Know-how und ihren Beitrag zu diesem Projekt.

Nils Franke

ED 13443
British Library Cataloguing-in-Publication Data.
A catalogue record for this book is available from the British Library
ISMN 979-0-2201-3278-0
ISBN 978-1-84761-260-1

CD recorded in Champs Hill, West Sussex, February 2012, on a Steinway D Concert Grand with Nils Franke, Piano
Producer: Ateş Orga
Editor and Engineer: Ken Blair
Cover image: Donaulandschaft bei Wien, ca. 1760. Johann Christian Brand (1722–1795). Source: The Yorck Project

French translation: Michaëla Rubi
German translation: Heike Brühl
Music setting and page layout: Darius Heise-Krzyszton, www.notensatzstudio.de

Printed in Germany S&Co.8762

Contents / Sommaire / Inhalt

The Pieces / Les pièces / Die Stücke

4

Introduction

The present collection of piano pieces is the third volume in a series of four books covering the piano music in the classical period from grades 1-8. It follows on from a format established in the *Romantic Piano Anthologies* Vols.1-4 (ED 12912 to ED 12915).

While anthologies are, inevitably, a personal selection of music they can nevertheless be underpinned by specific selection criteria. In the case of the present series, it has been my intention to include works that are idiomatically written, are indicative of their period and, above all, are useful in the development of pianistic skills for players at this stage of their development.

In the selection of repertoire I have tried to achieve a balance between established teaching pieces, rare works of the period, and between some of the main composers of the era and their lesser-known contemporaries. I hope that this can in some way attempt to reflect the diversity of styles within music from the 1780s to the 1820s.

The repertoire is presented broadly in an order of ascending difficulty, though I hope that the suggested sequence can be seen as a recommendation, rather than a restriction. The music included in this book is aimed at players of Grades 7–8 standard (UK) or intermediate to upper intermediate level (USA), or pianists of five to six years' playing experience (Europe).

The teaching notes are designed to assist students by offering some suggestions on how to approach a particular section within a piece. Also included are suggestions for topics that may need to be considered when playing classical piano music on a modern instrument, as the fortepiano of the late 18th century was of a different construction to the modern piano. The commentary cannot, and is not intended to, replace the collaborative spirit of exploration that teachers and students share in their lessons.

One of the most rewarding aspects of instrumental teaching is watching students become independent learners who make their own decisions and develop their own performance skills. I hope that the *Classical Piano Anthologies* can in some way contribute to this development.

Nils Franke

Introduction

Ce recueil de pièces pour piano constitue le troisième volet d'une collection en quatre volumes consacrés à la musique pour piano de la période classique, du niveau 1 au niveau 8. Du point de vue formel, il se calque sur le format établi dans l'*Anthologie du piano romantique*, volumes 1 à 4 (ED 12912 to ED 12915).

Le fait qu'une anthologie reflète inévitablement des choix personnels n'empêche pas qu'elle puisse être néanmoins sous-tendue par des critères de sélection spécifiques. Concernant la présente collection, j'ai choisi d'inclure des œuvres à l'écriture idiomatique, caractéristiques de leur période et, avant tout, utiles au développement des compétences pianistiques des instrumentistes à ce niveau de leur progression.

Pour ce qui concerne le choix du répertoire, j'ai tenté d'établir un équilibre, à la fois entre des pièces appartenant traditionnellement au répertoire pédagogique et des œuvres rares de cette période, et entre des compositeurs majeurs et leurs contemporains moins célèbres. J'espère que cela permettra, d'une certaine manière, d'illustrer la diversité des styles musicaux des années 1780 à 1820.

Globalement, le répertoire est présenté par ordre croissant de difficulté, mais j'espère que la progression proposée sera considérée davantage comme une suggestion que comme une contrainte. La musique proposée dans cet ouvrage s'adresse à des musiciens de niveau 7 à 8 standard (RU), intermédiaire à intermédiaire avancé (USA), ou à des pianistes possédant au moins cinq à six ans de pratique instrumentale (Europe).

Les notes pédagogiques ont pour objectif d'aider les élèves en leur suggérant des axes de travail dans l'approche de certains passages spécifiques à l'intérieur des morceaux. Dans la mesure où le pianoforte de la fin du 18e siècle était de facture différente du piano moderne, elles proposent également une réflexion sur les thématiques à aborder lorsque l'on joue de la musique classique sur un instrument moderne. Ces commentaires ne peuvent ni ne prétendent se substituer à l'esprit de collaboration et d'exploration que partagent le maître et l'élève pendant la leçon.

L'un des aspects les plus gratifiants de l'enseignement instrumental est de voir ses élèves devenir indépendants, expérimenter différentes pistes musicales et développer leurs propres dons. J'espère qu'à leur manière, ces *Anthologies du piano classique* pourront contribuer à ce développement.

Nils Franke

Einleitung

Die vorliegende Sammlung mit Klavierstücken ist der dritte Band einer vierbändigen Reihe mit klassischer Klaviermusik für alle Schwierigkeitsgrade. Sie ist genauso aufgebaut wie die *Romantic Piano Anthology* Bd. 1–4 (ED 12912 bis ED 12915).

Eine Anthologie enthält zwar immer eine subjektive Auswahl von Musikstücken, doch können natürlich bestimmte Auswahlkriterien herangezogen werden. Mein Anliegen bei der Zusammenstellung der vorliegenden Reihe war eine Auswahl von Musikstücken, die idiomatisch geschrieben, typisch für ihre Epoche und vor allem im Hinblick auf klavierspielerische Aspekte für Pianisten der jeweiligen Spielstufe nützlich sind.

Bei der Auswahl der Stücke habe ich versucht, ein ausgewogenes Verhältnis zwischen bewährtem Unterrichtsmaterial und selten gespielten klassischen Werken sowie zwischen einigen der wichtigsten Komponisten dieser Epoche und ihren weniger bekannten Zeitgenossen herzustellen. Ich hoffe, dass dies die Stilvielfalt der Musik von den 1780er- bis zu den 1820er-Jahren.

Die Stücke sind weitgehend nach aufsteigendem Schwierigkeitsgrad geordnet, wobei die vorgeschlagene Reihenfolge als Empfehlung und nicht als Einschränkung aufgefasst werden sollte. Die Stücke in diesem Buch richten sich an Spieler der Stufe 7–8 (Großbritannien), Mittelstufe bis obere Mittelstufe (USA) bzw. Pianisten mit mindestens fünf bis sechs Jahren Spielpraxis (Europa).

Die Spielhinweise sollen die Schüler mit Hilfe von Vorschlägen für bestimmte Passagen an das jeweilige Stück heranführen. Darüber hinaus enthält die Anthologie Vorschläge, die eventuell berücksichtigt werden müssen, wenn man klassische Klaviermusik auf einem modernen Instrument spielt, da sich das Pianoforte des späten 18. Jahrhunderts vom modernen Klavier unterschied. Die Anmerkungen können und sollen jedoch nicht die gemeinsame Beschäftigung von Lehrern und Schülern mit dem Stück im Unterricht ersetzen.

Eine der schönsten Belohnungen beim Unterrichten eines Instruments ist, zu beobachten, wie die Schüler unabhängig werden, eigene Entscheidungen treffen und ihren eigenen Spielstil entwickeln. Ich hoffe, dass die Bände der *Classical Piano Anthology* einen Betrag zu dieser Entwicklung leisten können.

Nils Franke

1. Etude
Op. 161 No. 8

Carl Czerny
(1791 – 1857)

Molto allegro
(♩ = 116)

*) Fingering by the composer

2. Keyboard Lesson No. 12

from 12 Keyboard Lessons

Allegro moderato
(♩ = 112)

Tommaso Giordani
(1733 – 1806)

8

3. Fugue

Op. 7

Prince Louis Ferdinand of Prussia
(1772 – 1806)

4. Etude

Op. 20 No. 3

Friedrich Kalkbrenner
(1785 – 1849)

5. Adagio

Hob. XV: 22/2

Joseph Haydn
(1732 – 1809)

Adagio ma non troppo
($\quad = 72$)

6. Alla tedesca

Craw 145

Johann Ladislav Dusík
(1760 – 1812)

Allegro
($\flat$. = 80)

7. Prestissimo

from Sonata Op. 17 No. 2

Johann Christian Bach
(1735 – 1782)

(♩. = 132)

28

8. Etude in E

Maria Szymanowska
(1789 – 1831)

9. Adagio
D.178

Franz Schubert
(1797 – 1828)

10. Allegretto
(WoO 53)

Allegretto
($\text{♩.} = 76$)

Ludwig van Beethoven
(1770 – 1827)

11. Adagio

KV 540

Wolfgang Amadeus Mozart
(1756 – 1791)

12. Eclogue
Op. 66 No. 3

Allegro con brio, ben marcato, ma sempre legato
(♩. = 76)

Vaclav Jan Tomáschek
(1774 – 1850)

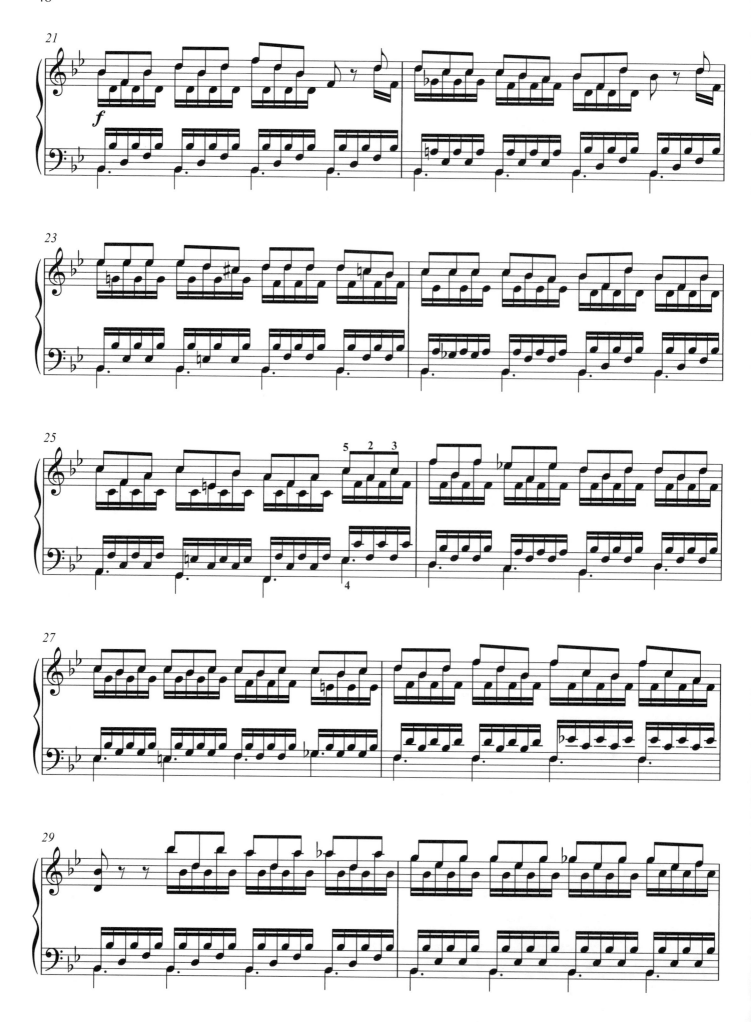

50

D. C. al Fine

Schott Music, London

Teaching Notes

One of the interesting challenges of playing music of this period is how we negotiate the difference between the fortepiano of the late 18th century and the piano of today. These differences are quite considerable, but incorporating the knowledge of period instruments while playing modern pianos can only enhance how we respond to the music. For example, the piano in the classical period had lighter keys (and fewer of them), strings that ran parallel to each other as opposed to being cross-strung, leather not felt on the hammers, slighter proportions, no metal frame (wooden instead) and a different action, too. All of this means that we can't recreate a sound as Haydn or Mozart may have heard it, but we can play the modern piano in a way that is respectful of these other musical textures. To achieve that, you might want to use sharply contrasted dynamic differences between *forte* and *piano*, and treat the right pedal as something that enhances the music at specific points, rather than being ever present. The basic sound quality should also be focused more on the treble of the instrument, rather than being bass orientated.

Ultimately, the concept of historically informed performance practice (being aware of and influenced by an understanding of how music of a different period may have been played) is an excellent basis for experimenting with music, for listening, evaluating and decision-making.

Carl Czerny (1791–1857)

1. Etude Op. 161 No. 8
(♩ = 116)

This Etude is an effective study in synchronizing finger work. Written excellently in a succession of hand positions, the piece calls for precise action from the knuckles so that both hands are coordinated effectively. Bars 3 to 4 imply the emphasising of two crotchet melodies that are embedded in the semiquavers:

The idea of combining a melody line with passage work is also present in the right hand of the quasi- cadential scoring of bars 8–11. The first notes of bar 11 should be placed as an arrival point. This moment of emphasis is musically important and technically welcome as it offers the player a slight moment's rest for repositioning the left hand on the second semiquaver of the bar.

Tommaso Giordani (c. 1730–1806)

2. Keyboard Lesson No. 12, from 12 Keyboard Lessons
(♩ = 112)

The title *Lesson No. 12* is somewhat misleading. Rather than take the term lesson literally, it is probably best understood to mean *Step or Session 12*; a term not indicative of music to be covered in the twelfth lesson but of the skills the composer expects students to develop at successive stages of their development.

In spirit, this music recalls early Haydn, and even the concept of providing unusual modulations is, at least in its tendency, rather Haydnesque. And yet listening to the piece it becomes clear that

Giordani's style is very much his own. Commencing the second half of the work (b. 31) in E minor, only to arrive at F sharp major two bars later is highly imaginative, maybe even slightly daring for its day.

The main challenges of the piece are the retaining of an effective right and left hand balance, especially when hand crossing is involved, as well as approaching the ornaments in a stylistically sympathetic way. Giordani himself suggested the following approach to the performance of trills (see **Appendix** p. 66).

Prince Louis Ferdinand of Prussia (1772–1806)

3. Fugue Op. 7
(♩ = 72)

This fugue occupies a unique position in the composer's output. Unusually for a pianist-composer, it was his only published piano work. Even more unusual for a performer known for his ability to improvise, a fugue appears to be a rather traditional composition for someone who is otherwise associated with the writing of sonata and rondo forms in chamber music of varying ensembles.

The present four part fugue contains some unexpectedly dramatic, if not unconventional moments. The sharp dynamic contrasts of bars 17 suggest that here is a piece eminently suitable for performance, rather than possibly academic study, as it is an engaging work that makes full use of the keyboard's sonority. The legato fingering is quite an important feature here. Do listen out for the dotted minims which need to be held in order to sustain the sonority of a part, particularly when forming the bass line (b.28ff).

Friedrich Kalkbrenner (1785–1849)

4. Etude Op. 20 No. 3
(♩. = c. 66 – composer's indication)

Kalkbrenner's *Etude* is a study in the balancing of three parts: a melody and bass line, complimented by the subtle rippling sound of an inner voice which supports but never dominates the musical texture. Do treat the melody line expressively by sometimes delaying the entry of the subsequent semiquavers. This can add to the clarity of the melody but also contribute to the pace and flow of the music. The study's ending in C sharp major leads (in its first edition) to a piece in that key, which explains the enharmonic change. The pedal marks are the composer's and need to be modified on a modern piano. When deciding on your approach to pedaling, follow the harmonic and /or melodic line of the piece.

Joseph Haydn (1732–1809)

5. Adagio, Hob. XV:22/2
(♩ = 72)

Haydn's *Adagio* is relatively late piece by the composer, dating from 1794. Much of the interest of the piece depends on the transparency of sound of the parts, so even in the opening bar there should be a clear difference between the held bass notes (crotchets) and the triplets of the tenor line. The hand crossing at the beginning of bar 19 should not sound rushed, and it is therefore better to take time than to attempt to play the top D in the right hand too soon. The scale in the right hand of bar 23 needs to be assembled carefully between hands so that the eleven notes are equally distributed over the three notes of the left. In bar 29 the octaves should continue to project a legato sound in the right hand, which may require some judicious use of the pedal. In bar 45 of the left hand there needs to be a silent change of finger to facilitate the fingering shown.

Jan Ladislav Dusík (1760–1812)

6. Alla tedesca, Craw 145
(♩. = 80)

Dusík's *Alla tedesca* is an excellent piece in which to observe rondo form in an applied sense. The composer uses the different sections to present a range of technical concepts, all of which are to be found in many pieces of the classical period. This is not, however, a criticism of the piece. Instead, the new textures in bars 17 and 38 enable the player to cover a range of classical playing techniques, but all within the context of one work. Section A of the rondo returns in bars 48 and 94, and the minor section is almost a text book interjection which adds much to the flavor of the work. Bars 64-90 need to be coordinated well between both hands but all of the writing lies well under the fingers, so the technical demands of the music are more manageable than one might assume initially. Even in the cadential writing of the last page, the feeling of two beats per bar should be maintained, so that the return to the A section is a seamless transition of textures.

Johann Christian Bach (1735–1782)

7. Prestissimo, from *Sonata Op. 17 No.2*
(♩. = 132)

Bach's *Sonata in C minor* is a three movement work of which the present prestissimo is the finale. The tempo indication, 'as fast as possible' may need some explanation. It is tempting to apply this to the fundamental pace of the piece, thereby steering the perception of tempo from the left hand line. But the texture Bach uses is in itself a busy sounding and largely continuous flow of quavers which, if audible, will do much to generate a sense of fast pace in themselves. In other words, if the left hand textures are present in performance, the underlying tempo need not be too fast for the music to sound *prestissimo*. The other indication of what a suitable practical tempo might be is the trill in the right hand in bar 11. For this to be clear, there has to be time for the notes to sound. Much of the sequential writing as seen in bars 1–10 is based on triadic patterns, and it is helpful to practise the piece wherever possible in four chords per bar, so the sequence of positions in the left hand becomes firmly established. This will aid the process of memorization, too. In bars 23-30 aim for a clearly defined first note in every group of three so that the rhythmic precision and the harmonic flow of the piece are maintained.

Maria Szymanovska (1789–1831)

8. Etude in E
(♩ = 108)

Maria Szymanovska's *Etude in E* is a cleverly written study that explores one motific idea which is gradually developed and expanded as the work progresses. This development is largely achieved by modulating through a range of keys, such as F major from bar 35 onwards, and the expansion of the music is facilitated by increasingly demanding textures. This is apparent in bars 55 onwards in which the right hand moves between two octaves, an approach to scoring that adds brilliance to the impression of the piece. This texture in particular will need careful preparation, especially as the right hand needs to be ready to play and in position before it is required. Play the sequence slowly and connect the moving of the right to the playing of the left hand notes, an idea that will enable you to move the right hand into position as quickly as possible.

Franz Schubert (1797–1828)

9. Adagio D.178
(♩ = 66)

Schubert's *Adagio D.178* is a self-contained character piece written by a 17 year old composer. The contrasting textures of the piece give the work an improvisatory feel, especially from bar 45 onwards. The fundamental tempo of the work at the beginning should take into account the subsequent textural changes. Bars 32 onwards needs a clear treble and bass line so that the three-layered texture of the music comes through. Play the quaver line in the thumb rather softly, so that is doesn't interfere with the transparency of the treble. Bars 55-57 and 68 should be played freely, but with close attention to the notation of the note values. Practising to play these bars in time will enable you to play them more freely thereafter whilst still retaining an awareness for their underlying rhythmic framework. The dynamic contrasts of bars 65 to 70 should be sharply characterized as there seem to be different characters at play. The *ff* gestures certainly need to be dramatic interjections that threated the otherwise calm mood of the music.

Ludwig van Beethoven (1770–1827)

10. Allegretto WoO 53
(♩. = 76)

Beethoven's *Allegretto WoO53* was originally intended as a movement of the piano sonata Op. 10 No.1 but was removed by Beethoven prior to publication of the sonata. The Allegretto exists in two versions, of which the present version is the second. The proximity to the sonata Op. 10 No. 1 is important though, as listening to this work will help the understanding of style and mood of the present piece. The quaver passage of bars 30–39 is best prepared in crotchets, but with the fingering that will be used when playing in quavers. This approach will support your harmonic understanding of the passage, and help your fingers to anticipate where to go next.

The *maggiore* section looks deceptively straight-forward but each hand needs to be prepared well as the flow of these notes should to be even in order to provide an effective contrast to the stormy outer sections of the work. Bars 40ff. can be divided up between the hands as indicated by the editorial fingering.

Wolfgang Amadeus Mozart (1756–1791)

11. Adagio KV 540
(♩ = 42)

Mozart's *Adagio in B minor* is a stand-alone work dated "Vienna, 1788" by the composer. Whether it was intended as a slow movement for an otherwise larger composition for piano remains unclear. However, the composer does list it as a single piece in his own work index which confirms that he presumably saw no need to compliment it with other musical material. A closer inspection of the Adagio reveals a beautifully crafted work of considerable musical variety. Just compare the way in which bars 1–6 and 15–21 are scored. The return of the main motif, but in a different key adds much to the timbral contrast of the music. The specific and sudden dynamic contrasts in the piece should be sharply articulated without sounding abrupt. After all, the fortepiano (the 'loud-soft' of the keyboard instruments) was still a relatively recent instrument which was only just replacing the harpsichord as the main keyboard instrument of its day.

The clarity of voicing is also a major feature of the piece, and the carefully considered part writing should be audible at all times. In bars 32 and 34 the dotted rhythm should be clearly articulated so that the music is kept moving by this figuration.

Václav Jan Tomášek (1774–1850)
12. Eclogue Op. 66 No. 3
($\downarrow$. = 76)

The concluding piece in this anthology, Tomaschek's *Eclogue*, is an excellent piece for performance which offers the opportunity to work on wrist rotation. For the piece to sound (and feel) effortless in performance, the steady flow of semiquavers should be generated by a slight sideways rotation towards the outer part of each hand, of which the second finger is rather like a linchpin. In other words, the relationship between the firmer melody line and the soft accompanimental semiquavers is generated by the knuckles that are supported by a flexible, slightly sideways moving wrist. The Trio section needs very little pedal, so the contrast between the held chords of the right hand and the shorter, rolled chords of the left is more clearly defined. When the music returns to the beginning of the piece, enjoy the main theme by letting the tempo build up gradually, rather than restarting the section at the speed of the opening.

Biographical Notes

Johann Christian Bach (1735–1782)
Johann Christian Bach was Johann Sebastian's youngest son. Following musical studies with his father, Johann Christian joined his older brother Carl Philip Emmanuel in Berlin to further his musical training. He then moved to Italy, becoming a cathedral organist in Milan in 1760. After writing church music and operas he moved to London in 1762 where he became the composer at the King's Theatre. Here Johann Christian became a highly successful member of society, whose portrait was painted twice by Gainsborough. Bach's most notable success must have been in his capacity as co-director of a highly regarded concert series with he organized together with CF Abel. Bach met the young Mozart in London in 1764 and both composers retained a fondness for each other's work throughout their lives. Johann Christian Bach's keyboard writing is a very interesting example of the incorporating of the (then) relatively recently developed pianoforte, for which he wrote in an elegant, early classical style. His piano sonatas Op. 5 (1766) and Op. 17 (1773/4) were published in Paris, Vienna, Amsterdam and London, a clear sign of the composer's popular appeal. He also co-wrote a piano method (1786) with Pasquale Ricci which demonstrates an excellent understanding of the developmental aspects of acquiring keyboard technique.

Ludwig van Beethoven (1770–1827)
Beethoven's influence on the direction of music in his time, as well as on the musical developments of subsequent composers, was considerable and multi-layered. His own stylistic development as a composer has resulted in the categorising of his output into three distinct periods: up to about 1802 (early), from 1802–1812 (middle), and from 1812 onwards (late). In terms of Beethoven's piano writing, these periods reflect the classical heritage of his initial phase, the development of his virtuoso keyboard style, and the subsequent structural, as well as technical individuality of his later works.

As a composer, Beethoven excelled in almost all forms of instrumental music, from the string quartet, the piano sonata, to the concerto and the symphony. The spontaneity, strength and emotional impact of his music were nevertheless the result of a meticulously crafted process of composition that is documented in detail in his sketchbooks and autographs. Beethoven was a successful performer as a pianist, though contemporary accounts of his playing differ in their assessment, depending on the focus of the writers. While some praised Beethoven's power and sound projection, others thought his playing to be messy and lacking control. What most sources agree upon though, is the impact Beethoven's playing made upon his listeners.

A piano work that unites both perspectives of his playing is the *Fantasy* for piano Op. 77; a work that is largely understood to be the written down version of an improvisation. It contains many Beethovenian features in harmony, melody and texture, and can as such offer a unique insight into the workings of this great musician. Beethoven's compositional achievements were so considerable that subsequent generations of composers from Schubert to Schumann, Liszt and Brahms hesitated for some time before writing in a genre that Beethoven had previously made his own.

Carl Czerny (1791–1857)
Czerny was, and remains, a significant figure in the development of pianism. Though predominantly remembered for being Beethoven's student and Liszt's teacher, Carl Czerny was an interesting composer in his own right. The systematic approach in which he developed his own collections of piano exercises was identical with the meticulous way in which he documented his studies with Beethoven, and his early impressions of Liszt. Unsurprisingly, it is in this context that he is mostly remembered. Czerny's own skills as a composer are possibly best encapsulated in two of his earlier works, the piano sonata Op. 7 (performed by Liszt in Paris in 1830) and his highly dramatic symphony in c minor. Aged 16, Czerny decided not to pursue a career as a performer, but to devote himself to teaching instead. This he did, often working for ten hours or more per day until he retired from teaching in 1836.

Czerny left arguably the most comprehensive teaching legacy of any pianist-tutor of his era, as set out in his *Pianoforte-Schule* Op. 500, a work he updated in 1846.

Jan Ladislav Dusík (1760–1812)
Dusík was born into a family of professional musicians. His father was an organist and composer, and Dusík's mother was a harpist, an instrument he also composed for. After initial studies at a Jesuit grammar school, he moved on to a grammar school in Prague, and

subsequently the city's university. This was followed by a period of appointments, concerts and studies across Europe, from Belgium (1779) to Hamburg, St. Petersburg and Lithuania. Dusík arrived in Paris in 1786. Here Marie Antoinette became one of his patrons before his urge to travel again took him to Milan in 1788. Returning briefly to Paris, just before the revolution, he settled in London in 1789. Here he stayed for some 10 years, teaching, composing and giving concerts. Dusík's employment by, and friendship with, Prince Louis Ferdinand of Prussia led to the composition of one of his most well-known piano works, the sonata in F sharp minor Op. 61, written in memory of the Prince in 1806.

Dusík's liking for music with programmatic ideas was certainly an influence on early 19th century composers but his achievements are more detailed than that. A comparison between textures found in Dusík's works and music written by some of his (subsequently) more well-known contemporaries document the originally of some of Dusík's motivic and harmonic invention.

Tommaso Giordani (c. 1730–1806)

Giordani was an Italian composer who spent much of his adult life in London and Dublin. Little is known for certain about the details of his early musical development but there are records of an opera of his, *La commediante fatta cantatrice*, having been performed in Covent Garden in 1756. In 1764 he moved to Dublin, returning to London some four years later as composer and musical director at the King's Theatre. In 1783 he once again moved to Dublin where he died in 1806. Like many musicians of his time, Giordani was involved in a range of musical activities, from composition to directing, teaching and organizing concerts, the entrepreneurial aspect of which contributed much to his income. Amongst his students was John Field (1782–1837) whose Nocturnes for piano were to have a lasting impact on 19th century piano music.

Joseph Haydn (1732–1809)

The evaluation of Haydn's position as a composer has undergone a number of changes over time. A popular perception of Haydn's life is the focus on the relative comfort and stability of his almost 30 year employment by the Esterhazy family in Eisenstadt near Vienna. Despite this comparatively settled existence (at least compared to that of many of his contemporaries, not least Mozart), Haydn's music was published widely post 1780, gaining its composer a growing national and international reputation. Visits to London from 1791 onwards confirmed his musical and economic successes.

However, his early years were very different. After initial training as a chorister and violinist, Haydn, who was not a virtuoso performer, survived by teaching and playing in ad hoc ensembles that provided music for functions. Compositionally, Haydn progressed slowly from being essentially self-taught to gaining the necessary skills. From the mid 1760s onwards Haydn developed a more distinctive musical style.

Haydn's output for piano covers over 60 sonatas, individual pieces, and variations. Though not a virtuoso keyboard performer, Haydn knew exactly how to write effectively for the fortepiano. All of his works lie very well under the fingers (irrespective of their varying degrees of complexity), but it is the element of surprise, both harmonically and in terms of pianistic textures, that gives many of the pieces their particular charm. Overall, Haydn's piano writing is never formulaic and therefore ever so slightly unpredictable.

Friedrich Kalkbrenner (1785–1849)

During his lifetime Kalkbrenner enjoyed the reputation of being one of the leading pianists of the period, a reputation he arguably shared with Johann Nepomuk Hummel during the 1820s.

After initial studies with his father, Kalkbrenner trained at the Paris Conservatoire before continuing his studies in Vienna from 1803 onwards. After a period of concertizing he settled in London in 1814 where he became a sought-after piano teacher. In 1825 Kalkbrenner returned to Paris as a wealthy and highly regarded pianist. Kalkbrenner's involvement in pedagogy was an important component of his Europe-wide reputation, so much so that even Chopin, after moving to Paris, considered having lessons with Kalkbrenner. In 1831 Kalkbrenner published a piano tutor book, his *Méthode* Op. 108, and even initiated a specialist training course for less experienced teachers. Somewhat more controversially from today's perspective, he marketed a hand tool (originally Johann Logier's) to support the establishing of good practice in the early learning stages of playing the piano. Designed to support the arm, its main purpose was to facilitate strength and independence of fingers.

Kalkbrenner's compositional output is largely for piano and covers a wide range of works from sonatas to smaller studies, written for the development of piano technique. The Etude included in this book is taken from his *24 Etudes dans tous les tons* op.20, published in 1816.

Wolfgang Amadeus Mozart (1756–1791)

Mozart was born into a highly musical environment. His father Leopold worked as an orchestral violinist and educator in Salzburg, and his older sister Nannerl had already shown her ability as a keyboard player. Mozart made rapid progress in his musical studies, so much so that his father decided to take him on a concert tour through Germany to London and Paris. These travels lasted for three and a half years before Mozart returned to Salzburg in 1766. Annual travels to Italy followed from 1769–72, enabling Mozart to come into contact with many other musicians, as indeed he did throughout his life. By the early 1780s Mozart seemed to have settled into life as a freelance musician in all its diversity. Some of his most successful piano concerti date from this period, as do many string quartets, some of which he played alongside their dedicatee, Joseph Haydn. By the end of the decade (and the beginning of the next) Mozart enjoyed considerable success as an opera composer with works such as *Cosi fan tutte* and *Die Zauberflöte*.

The diversity of Mozart's keyboard writing naturally reflects the different periods in the composer's life. Some of the earliest works date from when he was only five, a time when he wrote mostly shorter dances. His mature works include sonatas, variations and individual pieces, many of them written for his own use.

Prince Louis Ferdinand of Prussia (1772–1806)

Prince Louis Ferdinand of Prussia was the nephew of emperor Frederick the Great (1712–1786). A soldier by profession, Louis Ferdinand died in 1806 during the battle of Saalfeld, fighting the French Army of Napoleon.

Music had been an important part of Louis Ferdinand's upbringing (Frederick the Great was an excellent flautist), so much so that his musical legacy is documented on many different levels. Firstly, there is music dedicated to the Prince, including Beethoven's piano concerto Op. 37. Secondly, his own compositional work, particularly as the author of chamber music, earned the praise of his contemporaries, as well as subsequent generations. For example, Schumann played the Prince's piano chamber music, and Liszt wrote a work based on a theme by Louis Ferdinand. And thirdly, Louis Ferdinand's skills as an improviser were so well-known that reports survive of musical gatherings in salons, involving the improvising on two pianos alongside Jan Ladislav Dussek. The fugue in G minor included in this anthology (opus 7) is the Prince's only published work for solo piano.

Franz Schubert (1797–1828)

Schubert's initial musical training was provided by his father and brothers who taught him to play the piano, violin and viola. Aged 11 he was a awarded a choral scholarship that enabled him to study with Salieri. By the age of 16, Schubert decided to train as a teacher and a year later started work at his father's school. Aged 17, Schubert had written some of his early masterpieces, *Erlkönig* and *Gretchen am Spinnrade* for voice and piano. In 1816 Schubert relinquished his teaching post, choosing instead to live in the Viennese city centre and concentrating on composition. A period of financial uncertainty followed, in which Schubert wrote his first larger scale chamber music masterpiece, the *Trout quintet* (1819). In spring 1821 the success of the *Erlkönig* led to publications of his songs by Diabelli, and from it Schubert experienced a brief period of financial stability. From 1820-23 he was preoccupied by writing operatic music, a less than successful venture, only to turn to writing chamber and symphonic works for the last three years of his life.

Schubert's piano writing is, with few exceptions, not concerned with some of the outwardly technical components that some of his contemporaries employed. Instead, much of the music's demands arise from its preference of musical purpose over any form of pianistic consideration.

Maria Szymanovska (1789–1831)

Szymanovska was one of the most highly regarded female pianists of her time. Born in Warsaw, she concertized throughout Europe from the mid-1810s onwards, earning the praise of musicians and writers, including Johan Wolfgang von Goethe. From the late 1820s onwards she settled in St Petersburg where her salon attracted much social and artistic attention. As a composer, Szymanovska wrote piano music that reflected popular tastes of the time, including polonaises, waltzes, mazurkas, nocturnes, etudes and character pieces. Many of these works reveal an excellent understanding of piano technique, and of how to write effectively for the instrument.

Her private musical diary reveals the extent of her musical connections as it includes original contributions from Beethoven, Moscheles, Ogiński (see Classical Piano Anthology Volume 3, ED 13440) and many others.

Václav Jan Tomášek (1774–1850)

Tomášek was born in Skutec (Bohemia) in 1774. After initial lessons on violin and as a singer, he began to lean the organ. Tomášek's interests were far reaching as his studies of law, mathematics and aesthetics demonstrate. Despite having contact with the composer Kozeluh, Tomášek appears to have acquired most of his musical knowledge through the study of composition treatises, including the writings of Mattheson, Marpurg and Jirnberger. By 1806 Tomášek was appointed music tutor to the family of Count Buquoy in Prague. From the 1820s onwards, he lived as a much respected independent composer and teacher in Prague, where he occupied a central position amongst the city's musical elite. Tomášek was on friendly terms with Haydn and Beethoven, and his work as a teacher produced a lasting legacy. Amongst his pupils were the pianist Alexander Dreyschock (1818–1869), the musical writer Eduard Hanslick (1825–1904) and the composer Jan Václav Voříšek (1791–1825). Tomášek's most extensive contribution to the piano repertoire are the seven collections of *Eclogues*, predominantly lyrical character pieces, the textures of which anticipated some of Schubert's piano writing and elements of Mendelssohn's *Songs without words*.

Nils Franke

Bibliography

Hinson, Maurice.
Guide to the Pianist's Repertoire.
Bloomington and Indianapolis: Indiana University Press, 2000

MacGrath, Jane.
The Pianist's Guide to Standard Teaching and Performance Literature.
Van Nuys: Alfred Publishing Co., 1995

Prosnitz, Adolf.
Handbuch der Klavierliteratur.
Wien: Doblinger, 1908

Sadie, Stanley (ed.).
Grove Concise Dictionary of Music.
London: MacMillan Publishers, 1988

Sadie, Stanley (ed.)
Grove Dictionary of Music online.
[accessed 04/04/2011]

Wolters, Klaus.
Handbuch der Klavierliteratur zu zwei Händen.
Zürich und Mainz: Atlantis Musikbuch Verlag, 2001

Notes pédagogiques

L'un des enjeux intéressants dans l'interprétation de la musique de cette période pour les pianistes réside dans le traitement des différences entre le pianoforte de la fin du 18e siècle et le piano actuel. Ces différences sont assez considérables, mais notre connaissance des instruments d'époque ne peut qu'enrichir la réponse que nous apportons à cette musique lorsque nous la jouons sur un piano moderne. Par exemple, les touches du piano de la période classique étaient plus légères (et moins nombreuses), ses cordes disposées parallèlement et non croisées, ses marteaux recouverts de cuir et non de feutre ; le pianoforte était de proportions plus réduites, son cadre n'était pas en métal, mais en bois et son mécanisme était différent. Cela signifie que nous ne pouvons recréer les sonorités telles que Mozart ou Haydn les entendaient, mais nous pouvons jouer du piano moderne dans le respect de ces textures musicales différentes. Afin d'y parvenir, il faudra user de contrastes dynamiques très différenciés entre *piano* et *forte* et traiter la pédale de droite comme un moyen d'enrichir ponctuellement la musique plutôt que l'utiliser en permanence. Fondamentalement, la qualité sonore devra être axée davantage sur les aigus de l'instrument que sur les graves.

Enfin, le concept d'une pratique musicale historiquement éclairée (conscience et influence de la compréhension des pratiques musicales d'une époque différente) constitue une excellente base pour l'expérimentation musicale, l'écoute, l'évaluation et les choix musicaux.

Carl Czerny (1791–1857)
1. Etude Op. 161 No. 8
($\quad$ = 116)

Cette étude permet de travailler efficacement la synchronisation des doigts. Remarquablement écrite dans une succession de positions des mains différentes, cette pièce requiert des mouvements précis des articulations afin de coordonner efficacement les deux mains. Deux motifs mélodiques de noires au sein des groupes de doubles-croches devront être mis en exergue aux mesures 3 et 4 :

L'idée d'allier une ligne mélodique à des passages virtuoses est également présente à la main droite des mesures 8–11 dont l'écriture est quasiment cadentielle.

Le premier accord de la mesure 11 sera interprété comme un point d'arrivée. Cette accentuation est importante musicalement et bienvenue techniquement, car elle offre à l'instrumentiste un court moment de répit pour repositionner la main gauche sur la deuxième double-croche de la mesure.

Tommaso Giordani (env. 1730–1806)
2. Keyboard Lesson No. 12, tiré de *12 Keyboard Lessons*
($\quad$ = 112)

Le terme de *Leçon No. 12* est quelque peu trompeur. Plutôt que de le prendre au pied de la lettre, il serait sans doute plus juste d'y

voir une 12ᵉ étape ou séance, c'est-à-dire un terme ne désignant pas du répertoire devant être abordé lors de la douzième leçon, mais les compétences dont le compositeur attend qu'elles soient développées par les élèves aux différents stades de leur évolution.

L'esprit de cette musique rappelle celui des premières compositions de Haydn. Même le concept des modulations inhabituelles est plutôt haydnien, du moins dans son inspiration. Pourtant, à l'écoute de cette pièce, il est évident que Giordani possède son propre style. Commencer la seconde partie de l'œuvre (mes. 31) en *mi* mineur pour aboutir en *fa* dièse majeur deux mesures plus loin est un procédé très inventif voire relativement osé pour son époque. Les principaux défis à relever ici sont le maintien d'un véritable équilibre main droite main gauche, en particulier en cas de croisements de mains, ainsi qu'une approche des ornements compatible du point de vue stylistique. Giordani lui-même suggérait d'exécuter les trilles de la manière suivante (**Annex**: p. 66)

Prince Louis-Ferdinand de Prusse (1772–1806)
3. Fugue Op. 7
($\quad$ = 72)

Cette fugue occupe une place atypique dans l'œuvre de Louis-Ferdinand de Prusse. Effectivement, fait rare pour un compositeur pianiste, il s'agit de son unique œuvre pour piano publiée. De même, pour un interprète aux qualités d'improvisateur reconnues et un compositeur signant habituellement des œuvres de musique de chambre de forme sonate et rondo, la fugue apparaît comme une composition plutôt traditionnelle.

Cette fugue à quatre voix contient quelques passages assez originaux, au caractère dramatique inattendu. Les contrastes dynamiques marqués des mesures 17 suggèrent qu'il s'agit d'une pièce éminemment adaptée au répertoire de concert plutôt que d'une étude académique. C'est une œuvre exigeante utilisant toutes les sonorités du clavier dans laquelle le legato occupe une place importante. Veillez à bien tenir les blanches pointées afin de soutenir chaque partie, en particulier lorsqu'elles sont à la basse (mesures 28ss).

Friedrich Kalkbrenner (1785–1849)
4. Etude Op. 20 No. 3
($\quad$ = c. 66 – indication du compositeur)

Cette étude de Kalkbrenner est axée sur l'équilibre entre trois parties : une mélodie, une ligne de basse et une voix intermédiaire les soutenant subtilement sans jamais dominer la texture musicale. Traitez la mélodie de manière expressive en retenant parfois l'entrée des doubles croches correspondantes. Ce procédé apportera de la clarté à la mélodie et contribuera également à donner du mouvement à la musique. L'étude était suivie (dans sa première édition) d'une pièce en *ut* dièse majeur, d'où l'enharmonie à la fin. Les indications de pédale sont du compositeur et nécessitent d'être adaptées au piano moderne. Votre approche de l'utilisation des pédales devra être en accord avec la ligne harmonique et/ou mélodique de la pièce.

Joseph Haydn (1732–1809)
5. Adagio, Hob. XV:22/2
($\quad$ = 72)

Daté de 1794, l'*Adagio* de Haydn est une pièce relativement tardive du compositeur. Une grande partie de l'intérêt de cette pièce repose sur la transparence sonore de chaque partie. Ainsi, dès la mesure d'ouverture, les notes tenues de la basse (noires) et les triolets de la voix de ténor devront être clairement différenciés. Le croisement de mains au début de la mesure 19 ne doit pas être précipité, mieux valant prendre son temps plutôt que de jouer trop tôt le *ré* aigu à la main droite. Le trait de la mesure 23 à la main droite doit être pensé avec soin afin que ces onze notes se distribuent de manière égale au-dessus des trois notes de la main gauche. À la mesure 29, les octaves à la main droite sonneront *legato*, éventuellement grâce à un usage judicieux de la pédale. La mesure 45 nécessite un changement de doigt silencieux à la main gauche afin de faciliter l'application du doigté indiqué.

Jan Ladislav Dusík (1760–1812)
6. Alla tedesca, Craw 145
(♩. = 80)

Le *Alla tedesca* de Dusík est une excellente application de la forme rondo permettant de se familiariser davantage avec cette dernière. Le compositeur utilise les différentes parties du rondo pour présenter un éventail de concepts techniques également présents dans de nombreuses autres pièces de la période classique. Il ne s'agit pas là d'une critique, au contraire. Aux mesures 17 et 38, de nouvelles textures permettent à l'instrumentiste de travailler une série de techniques de jeu classiques, en les plaçant toutes dans le contexte d'une œuvre. La partie A réapparaît aux mesures 48 à 94 et la partie en mineur, comme une sorte d'interjection, apporte beaucoup de saveur à l'œuvre. Les mesures 64–90 nécessitent une bonne coordination des mains, mais l'ensemble vient bien sous les doigts et les exigences techniques de cette pièce sont plus faciles à surmonter qu'on pourrait le penser au départ. La sensation de deux pulsations par mesure sera maintenue y compris dans l'écriture cadentielle de la dernière page afin que la transition entre les différentes textures se fasse en douceur au retour de la partie A.

Johann Christian Bach (1735–1782)
7. Prestissimo, tiré de la *Sonate Op. 17 No. 2*
(♩. = 132)

La *Sonate en do mineur* de Bach est une œuvre en trois mouvements dont le Prestissimo présenté ici constitue le mouvement final. L'indication de tempo « aussi rapide que possible » nécessite peut-être une explication. Il est tentant de l'appliquer au mouvement général de la pièce, faisant naître la perception du tempo à partir de la ligne de la main gauche. Mais la texture utilisée par Bach est suffisamment dense en elle-même, avec son flux continu de croches. S'il est audible, ce dernier contribuera largement, par sa nature même, à la sensation de rapidité. En d'autres termes, si les textures de la main gauche sont présentes dans l'interprétation, le tempo général n'aura pas besoin d'être trop rapide pour donner une impression de *prestissimo*. Le trille de la mesure 10 à la main droite peut également servir d'indicateur en matière de tempo. Pour que ce trille sonne correctement, les notes doivent avoir le temps de résonner. Une grande part de l'écriture séquentielle telle qu'on la trouve aux mesures 1–9 se fonde sur des accords de trois notes. Il sera utile de s'entraîner à jouer ce passage et les passages similaires en plaquant quatre accords par mesure afin que la séquence de positions à la main gauche soit fermement ancrée. Le processus de mémorisation s'en trouvera également favorisé. Aux mesures 23–30, veillez à attaquer clairement la première de chaque groupe de trois notes afin de maintenir la précision rythmique et le flux harmonique.

Maria Szymanovska (1789–1831)
8. Etude en mi
(♩ = 108)

De conception brillante, l'*Étude en mi* de Maria Szymanovska explore une idée de motif qui se développe et s'épanouit progressivement tout au long de l'œuvre. La modulation dans toute une série de tonalités, par exemple *fa* majeur à partir de la mesure 35, participe largement au développement de cette idée tandis que celle-ci s'épanouit dans des textures toujours plus exigeantes. On le voit notamment à partir de la mesure 55, où la main droite couvre deux octaves, une approche de l'écriture renforçant l'impression virtuose donnée par la pièce. Cette texture en particulier nécessitera une préparation soigneuse, notamment parce que la main droite doit atteindre la bonne position et se tenir prête à jouer avant que cela soit nécessaire. Jouez ce passage lentement et connectez les déplacements de la main droite aux notes de la main gauche, ce qui vous permettra de placer votre main droite dans la bonne position le plus rapidement possible.

Franz Schubert (1797–1828)
9. Adagio D.178
(♩ = 66)

Composé par Schubert alors qu'il n'était âgé que de 17 ans, l'*Adagio D.178* est une pièce de caractère indépendante à laquelle des textures contrastantes confèrent un certain air d'improvisation, notamment à partir de la mesure 45. Le tempo général de l'œuvre doit tenir compte de ces changements de texture dès le début. À partir de la mesure 32, la clarté de la ligne supérieure et de la ligne inférieure est importante pour mettre en valeur la texture à trois voix de la musique. La ligne de croches au pouce sera jouée avec douceur afin de ne pas interférer avec la transparence de la ligne supérieure. Les mesures 55–57 et 68 seront jouées librement, mais en portant une grande attention aux valeurs de notes telles qu'elles sont écrites. Vous entraîner à jouer ces mesures en rythme vous permettra par conséquent de les jouer avec davantage de liberté tout en ayant conscience de leur cadre rythmique sous-jacent. Les contrastes dynamiques des mesures 65 à 70 devront être bien caractérisés puisqu'il semble que s'expriment ici plusieurs personnages. Les *ff* interviendront comme autant d'interjections dramatiques menaçant la nature par ailleurs plutôt calme de la musique.

Ludwig van Beethoven (1770–1827)
10. Allegretto WoO 53
(♩. = 76)

Initialement, l'*Allegretto WoO53* devait constituer l'un des mouvements de la S*onate pour piano Op. 10 No. 1*, mais Beethoven l'en exclut avant la publication. L'*Allegretto* existe dans deux versions dont celle-ci est la seconde. Sa proximité avec la sonate op. 10 no 1 est un facteur important, car l'écoute de cette dernière facilitera la compréhension du style et de l'esprit de l'*Allegretto*. Pour une meilleure préparation, le passage en croches des mesures 30–39 sera travaillé sur des noires, en conservant toutefois les mêmes doigtés que lorsqu'il est joué en croches. Cette approche permettra d'améliorer votre compréhension harmonique de ce passage et vous aidera à anticiper les positions des doigts.

Les passages marqués *maggiore* semblent trompeusement faciles, mais chaque main devra être bien préparée afin que le mouvement des notes soit serein et régulier et constitue un véritable contraste par rapport à l'agitation des parties extrêmes. Les mesures 40 ss. seront réparties entre les deux mains comme l'indiquent les doigtés proposés par l'éditeur.

Wolfgang Amadeus Mozart (1756–1791)
11. Adagio KV 540
($\downarrow$ = 42)

L'*Adagio en si mineur* de Mozart est une œuvre isolée datée « Vienne, 1788 » par son auteur. Il n'a pas été établi s'il était censé constituer le mouvement lent d'une œuvre pour piano de plus grande envergure. Toutefois, le compositeur l'inscrivit isolément dans son index personnel, soulignant ainsi qu'il ne voyait probablement pas la nécessité de le compléter par d'autres matériaux musicaux. Une observation plus attentive de l'*Adagio* révèle une œuvre de facture magnifique dénotant une variété musicale considérable. Il suffit de comparer l'écriture des mesures 1–6 et 15–21. Le retour du motif principal dans un registre différent participe beaucoup au contraste des timbres. Ces contrastes subits très spécifiques devront être articulés avec précision, mais sans brusquerie. Après-tout, le piano-forte (instrument « doux et fort » de la famille des claviers) restait alors un instrument relativement récent qui venait juste de supplanter le clavecin en tant que principal instrument à clavier.

L'écriture soigneuse des différentes parties devra être perceptible en permanence tant la clarté des voix est un aspect majeur de cette pièce.

Dans le mesure 32 à 34 le rythme pointé devra être articulé particulièrement clairement afin que cette figure puisse continuer à imprimer son mouvement à la musique.

Václav Jan Tomášek (1774–1850)
12. Eclogue Op. 66 No. 3
($\downarrow$. = 76)

L'*Eclogue* de Tomášchek, pièce finale de cette anthologie, est une œuvre parfaitement adaptée au concert qui offre l'occasion de travailler la rotation du poignet. Afin que la pièce sonne (et soit exécutée) sans effort, la régularité du mouvement de doubles croches sera générée grâce à une légère rotation latérale des poignets vers l'extérieur de la main, pour laquelle le deuxième doigt jouera en quelque sorte le rôle de pivot. En d'autres termes, la relation entre la fermeté de la ligne mélodique et la douceur des doubles croches de l'accompagnement repose sur les articulations elles-mêmes soutenues par un mouvement souple et légèrement latéral du poignet. La partie en trio nécessite très peu de pédale, ainsi le contraste entre les accords tenus de la main droite et les accords plus brefs, arpégés de la main gauche sera-t-il plus clairement défini. Lors de la reprise au début de la pièce, profitez du thème principal pour revenir progressivement dans le tempo plutôt qu'en reprenant directement à la vitesse initiale.

Notes biographiques

Johann Christian Bach (1735–1782)
Johann Christian Bach était le plus jeune fils de Johann Sébastian Bach. Il commença à étudier la musique auprès de son père puis rejoignit son grand frère Carl Philip Emmanuel à Berlin pour continuer sa formation musicale. Il s'installa ensuite en Italie où il devint organiste à la cathédrale de Milan en 1760. Après avoir écrit de la musique sacrée et des opéras, il s'installa à Londres en 1762, y occupant les fonctions de compositeur au King's Theatre et devenant un membre très en vue de la société dont Gainsborough fit le portrait par deux fois. Son succès le plus notable tient sans doute à ses compétences en tant que co-directeur, aux côtés de CF Abel, d'une série de concerts très appréciés. Il rencontra le jeune Mozart à Londres en 1764 et les deux compositeurs conservèrent toute leur vie un intérêt mutuel pour leur travail. Les œuvres pour claviers de Johann Christian Bach constituent un exemple très intéressant de l'intégration du pianoforte dont le développement était (alors) relativement récent et pour lequel il écrivit dans le style élégant des débuts du classicisme. Ses sonates pour piano op. 5 (1766) et op. 17 (1773/4) furent publiées à Paris, Vienne, Amsterdam et Londres, signe manifeste de la popularité de leur auteur. Il a également co-écrit avec Pasquale Ricci une méthode de piano (1786) qui dénote une excellente compréhension du développement de la technique pianistique.

Ludwig van Beethoven (1770–1827)
L'influence de Beethoven sur la musique de son temps ainsi que sur le développement des compositeurs de la génération suivante a été considérable et multiple. Son propre développement stylistique en tant que compositeur débouche sur un classement de sa production en trois périodes distinctes : jusqu'à environ 1802 (première période), de 1802 à 1812 (période intermédiaire) et à partir de 1812 (période tardive). En termes d'écriture pianistique, ces périodes reflètent l'héritage classique de la phase initiale, le développement de son style virtuose au clavier et l'individualité structurelle et technique qui en a découlé dans ses œuvres plus tardives.

En tant que compositeur, Beethoven excellait dans presque toutes les formes de musique instrumentale, du quatuor à cordes et de la sonate pour piano au concerto et à la symphonie. La spontanéité, la force et l'impact émotionnel de sa musique sont cependant le résultat d'un processus de composition méticuleux, documenté en détail grâce à ses carnets d'esquisses et ses manuscrits. Beethoven était un pianiste-interprète reconnu, bien que les témoignages contemporains sur sa façon de jouer diffèrent selon le point de vue de leur auteur. Tandis que certains louent sa puissance et la projection du son, d'autres trouvent son jeu brouillon et manquant de contrôle. Cependant, l'impact du jeu de Beethoven sur ses auditeurs est un point sur lequel la plupart des sources s'accordent.

La fantaisie pour piano op. 77 est une œuvre réunissant ces deux perspectives de jeu. Souvent considérée comme la version écrite d'une improvisation, elle contient de nombreux éléments caractéristiques de l'écriture de Beethoven du point de vue de l'harmonie, de la mélodie et de la texture, et en tant que telle, offre un aperçu unique des mécanismes d'écriture de ce grand musicien.

Les réalisations musicales de Beethoven sont si considérables que les générations suivantes de compositeurs, de Schubert à Schumann, Liszt et Brahms ont hésité un certain temps avant d'écrire dans un genre que Beethoven s'était approprié avant eux.

Carl Czerny (1791–1857)
Czerny fut et demeure une figure significative du développement de l'art pianistique. Bien que sa mémoire soit surtout associée à Beethoven pour avoir été son élève, ainsi qu'à Liszt pour avoir été son professeur, Carl Czerny est un compositeur intéressant pour lui-même. Cependant, l'approche systématique qu'il appliqua au développement de ses propres recueils d'exercices pour le piano étant identique à la façon méticuleuse dont il documenta ses cours avec Beethoven et ses premières impressions de Liszt, il n'est pas

surprenant qu'on se souvienne davantage de lui dans ce contexte. Deux œuvres de jeunesse de Czerny, sa sonate pour piano op. 7 (interprétée par Liszt à Paris en 1830) et sa symphonie très dramatique en *ut* mineur, sont peut-être les meilleurs témoins de ses dons personnels en tant que compositeur. À l'âge de 16 ans, il décida de ne pas poursuivre sa carrière de concertiste, mais de se consacrer en lieu et place à l'enseignement. C'est ce qu'il fit, travaillant souvent dix heures et plus par jour, jusqu'à sa retraite en 1836. Parmi tous les pianistes de son temps, Czerny est sans conteste celui qui laissa l'héritage pédagogique le plus exhaustif, comme en témoigne sa *Pianoforte-Schule* op. 500, ouvrage qu'il mit à jour en 1846.

Jan Ladislav Dusík (1760–1812)

Dusík était issu d'une famille de musiciens professionnels, d'un père organiste et compositeur et d'une mère harpiste, un instrument pour lequel il composa aussi par la suite. Après des études initiales dans une école de jésuites, il entra dans un lycée à Prague puis à l'université de cette ville. Vint ensuite une période d'études, d'engagements et de concerts dans toute l'Europe, de la Belgique (1779) à Hambourg et Saint-Pétersbourg en passant par la Lituanie. En 1786, Dusík arriva à Paris où Marie-Antoinette devint l'une de ses protectrices, jusqu'à ce que son besoin de voyager l'entraîne à Milan. Il revint brièvement à Paris juste avant la Révolution puis s'installa à Londres en 1789 où il resta 10 ans, enseignant, composant et donnant des concerts. Son service auprès du prince Louis-Ferdinand de Prusse et l'amitié qui les liait donna lieu à la composition de l'une de ses œuvres pour piano les plus connues, la sonate en *fa* dièse mineur op. 61, écrite en mémoire du prince en 1806.

Le goût de Dusík pour la musique à programme exerça certainement une influence sur les compositeurs du début du 19e siècle, mais ses réalisations sont plus détaillées. Une comparaison entre les textures relevées dans ses œuvres et celles de certains de ses contemporains qui connurent plus tard davantage de notoriété, documente l'originalité d'invention de Dusík en termes de motifs et d'harmonie.

Tommaso Giordani (env. 1730–1806)

Compositeur italien, Giordani passa une grande partie de sa vie d'adulte à Londres et Dublin. Peu d'éléments concrets nous sont parvenus sur ses débuts musicaux, mais certains documents attestent qu'un opéra de sa composition, *La commediante fatta cantatrice*, fut donné à Covent Garden en 1756. Il s'installa à Dublin en 1764 et revint à Londres quatre ans plus tard en tant que compositeur et directeur musical du King's Theatre. En 1783, il retourna définitivement à Dublin où il mourut en 1806. Comme de nombreux musiciens de son temps, Giordani était impliqué dans toute une série d'activités musicales, de la composition à la direction, de l'enseignement à l'organisation de concerts, dont l'aspect commercial contribuait largement à ses revenus. Il eut parmi ses élèves John Field (1782–1837), dont les nocturnes pour piano ont exercé une influence durable sur la musique de piano du 19e siècle.

Joseph Haydn (1732–1809)

L'estimation de la place de Haydn en tant que compositeur a été soumise à de nombreuses variations au gré du temps. La perception populaire de sa vie se focalise souvent sur le relatif confort et la stabilité de ses presque 30 ans d'engagement auprès de la famille Esterhazy à Eisenstadt, près de Vienne. Malgré une existence effectivement relativement sédentaire (du moins par rapport à nombre de ses contemporains, et notamment à Mozart), la musique de Haydn fut largement publiée après 1780, lui permettant ainsi de jouir d'une réputation nationale et internationale croissante. À partir de 1791, ses visites à Londres vinrent confirmer ses succès économiques et musicaux.

Pourtant, ses premières années avaient été très différentes. Après une formation initiale de choriste et de violoniste, Haydn, qui n'était pas un virtuose, survécut en donnant des cours et en intégrant des ensembles jouant de la musique fonctionnelle. Du point de vue de la composition, essentiellement autodidacte, il progressa lentement jusqu'à acquérir les compétences nécessaires qui lui permirent, à partir du milieu des années 1760, de développer un style musical plus caractéristique.

La production pour piano de Haydn comprend plus de 60 sonates, pièces individuelles et variations. Bien que n'étant pas virtuose, il savait exactement comment écrire efficacement pour le pianoforte. Toutes ses œuvres viennent très bien sous les doigts (quel que soit leur degré de complexité), mais c'est l'élément de surprise, à la fois en termes d'harmonie et de texture pianistique, qui donne leur charme particulier à nombre de ses compositions. L'écriture pianistique de Haydn n'obéit jamais à des formules et garde ainsi toujours un caractère légèrement imprévisible.

Friedrich Kalkbrenner (1785–1849)

De son vivant, Kalkbrenner était considéré comme l'un des pianistes majeurs de son temps. Il est sans doute raisonnable de suggérer qu'au cours des années 1820, Johann Nepomuk Hummel et Kalkbrenner se partagèrent à égalité la réputation de compter parmi les interprètes de pianoforte les plus accomplis.

Après avoir commencé ses études avec son père, Kalkbrenner entra au conservatoire de Paris puis poursuivit sa formation à Vienne à partir de 1803. Ensuite, à l'issue d'une période de concerts, il s'installa à Londres entre 1814 et 1833, où il devint un professeur de piano très recherché. Il mit également au point un « guide-main », c'est-à-dire un outil (conçu initialement par Johann Logier) destiné à favoriser les bonnes pratiques aux premiers stades de l'apprentissage du piano. En 1825, alors pianiste florissant et également précédé d'une excellente réputation d'enseignant, Kalkbrenner retourna s'installer à Paris.

Sa production est largement consacrée au piano et couvre un vaste éventail d'œuvres, de la sonate à l'étude d'envergure modeste écrite pour le développement de la technique pianistique.

Wolfgang Amadeus Mozart (1756–1791)

Mozart naquit dans un environnement très musical. Son père Léopold était pédagogue et violoniste dans un orchestre à Salzbourg tandis que sa grande sœur, Nannerl, avait déjà révélé ses capacités au piano. Mozart fit des progrès rapides dans ses études musicales, à tel point que son père décida de l'emmener dans une tournée de concerts en l'Allemagne, puis à Londres et Paris. Ces voyages durèrent trois ans et demi avant que Mozart s'installe à Salzbourg en 1766. S'ensuivirent entre 1769 et 1772 des voyages annuels en Italie, qui permirent à Mozart d'entrer en contact avec de nombreux autres musiciens, comme il le fit tout au long de sa vie. Au début des années 1780, il semble que Mozart se soit établi comme musicien indépendant, avec tout ce que cela implique. Certains de ses concertos pour piano les plus célèbres datent de cette période, ainsi que nombre de ses quatuors à cordes dont il interpréta certain avec Joseph Haydn, leur dédicataire. À la fin de cette décennie (et au début de la suivante), Mozart rencontra un succès considérable comme compositeur d'opéra, avec des œuvres comme *Cosi fan tutte* et *La flûte enchantée*.

La diversité de ses œuvres pour piano reflète naturellement les différentes périodes de la vie du compositeur. Certaines parmi les plus précoces ont été écrites alors qu'il était à peine âgé de 5 ans, une époque où il écrivait principalement de courtes danses. Les œuvres de sa maturité incluent sonates, variations et pièces individuelles écrites le plus souvent à son usage personnel.

Prince Louis-Ferdinand de Prusse (1772–1806)

Le prince Louis-Ferdinand de Prusse était le neveu de l'empereur Frédéric le Grand (1712–1786). Soldat de profession, Louis-Ferdinand mourut en 1806 pendant la bataille de Saalfeld contre l'armée française de Napoléon.

La musique occupa une place importante dans l'éducation de Louis-Ferdinand (Frédéric le Grand était un excellent flûtiste), tant et si bien que son héritage musical revêt de multiples facettes. En premier lieu, des œuvres dédiées au prince dont notamment le concerto pour piano op. 37 de Beethoven. En second lieu, ses propres compositions musicales qui recueillirent la faveur de ses contemporains ainsi que des générations suivantes, en particulier dans le domaine de la musique de chambre. Schumann par exemple jouait des œuvres de chambre du prince et Liszt écrivit une œuvre à partir de l'un de ses thèmes. Enfin, les talents d'improvisateur de Louis-Ferdinand étaient tellement connus que certains témoignages évoquent des salons musicaux où il improvisait avec Jan Ladislav Dussek sur deux pianos. La fugue en *sol* mineur présentée dans cette anthologie (opus 7) est son unique œuvre publiée pour piano seul.

Franz Schubert (1797–1828)

La formation musicale initiale de Schubert lui a été prodiguée par son père et par ses frères qui lui enseignèrent le piano, le violon et l'alto. À l'âge de 11 ans, il bénéficia d'une bourse d'études qui lui permit de se former auprès de Salieri. Ensuite, à 16 ans, Schubert décida de se former à l'enseignement et commença un an plus tard à travailler dans l'école de son père. À 17 ans, il avait écrit certains de ses premiers chefs-d'œuvre, dont *Le Roi des aulnes* et *Marguerite au rouet*, pour voix et piano. En 1816, Schubert abandonna son poste d'enseignant et choisit de vivre au centre de Vienne et de se consacrer à la composition. S'ensuivit une période d'incertitude financière, mais à la fin de 1819, Schubert écrivit son premier chef-d'œuvre de musique de chambre, son quintette intitulé *La Truite*. Au printemps 1821, le succès du *Roi des aulnes* déboucha sur la publication de ses airs par Diabelli, qui lui permit de connaître une courte période de stabilité financière. De 1820 à 1823, il se lança dans l'écriture de musique d'opéra, une entreprise malheureusement peu fructueuse, pour finalement se tourner vers l'écriture de musique de chambre et de musique symphonique les trois dernières années de sa vie. À quelques rares exceptions près, l'écriture pianistique de Schubert ne se préoccupe pas d'effets techniques tels que le font certains de ses contemporains. Au contraire, toutes les exigences de sa musique proviennent de la prééminence du propos musical sur toute autre forme de considération pianistique.

Maria Szymanovska (1789–1831)

Szymanovska était l'une des pianistes féminines les plus en vue de son époque. Née à Varsovie, elle se produisit en concert dans toute l'Europe à partir du milieu des années 1810, et fut plébiscitée tant par les musiciens que par les écrivains, parmi lesquels Wolfgang von Goethe. À la fin des années 1820, elle s'installa à Saint-Pétersbourg où son salon devint un centre d'attraction sociale et artistique. En tant que compositeur, Szymanovska écrivait de la musique pour piano reflétant les goûts de l'époque, notamment des polonaises, des valses, des mazurkas, des nocturnes, des études et des pièces de caractère. Un grand nombre de ces œuvres dénotent

une excellente compréhension de la technique du piano et de l'art d'écrire efficacement pour cet instrument.

Son journal musical personnel révèle l'étendue de son réseau de relations dans le monde de la musique, incluant des contributions originales de Beethoven, Moscheles, Oginski (voir Anthologie du piano classique volume 3, ED 13440) et bien d'autres.

Václav Jan Tomášek (1774–1850)

Tomášek naquit à Skutec (Bohème) en 1774. Après ses premières leçons de violon et de chant, il commença à s'orienter vers l'orgue. Tomášek avait de nombreux centres d'intérêt comme en témoignent ses études en droit, en mathématiques et en esthétique. Malgré ses contacts avec le compositeur Kozeluh, Tomášek semble avoir acquis la plupart de ses connaissances musicales par l'étude de traités de composition, notamment les écrits de Mattheson, Marpurg et Jirnberger. En 1806, Tomášek fut nommé maître de musique auprès de la famille du comte Buquoy à Prague. Puis, à partir des années 1820, il vécut à Prague où il occupait une position centrale au sein de l'élite musicale de la ville en tant que compositeur indépendant et professeur hautement respecté. Tomášek entretenait des liens d'amitié avec Haydn et Beethoven et a laissé un héritage vivace en tant que professeur. Parmi ses élèves comptent le pianiste Alexander Dreyschock (1818–1869), le critique musical Eduard Hanslick (1825–1904) et le compositeur Jan Václav Voříšek (1791–1825). La contribution la plus importante de Tomášek au répertoire de piano consiste en ses sept recueils d'*Eclogues*. Ceux-ci sont des pièces de caractère essentiellement lyrique, dont les textures préfigurent certaines compositions de Schubert pour piano ainsi que certains éléments des *Romances sans paroles* de Mendelssohn.

Nils Franke

Bibliographie

Hinson, Maurice.
Guide to the Pianist's Repertoire.
Bloomington et Indianapolis: Indiana University Press, 2000

MacGrath, Jane.
The Pianist's Guide to Standard Teaching and Performance Literature.
Van Nuys: Alfred Publishing Co., 1995

Prosnitz, Adolf.
Handbuch der Klavierliteratur.
Vienne: Doblinger, 1908

Sadie, Stanley (éd.).
Grove Concise Dictionary of Music.
Londres: MacMillan Publishers, 1988

Sadie, Stanley (ed.)
Grove Dictionary of Music online.
[consulté 04/04/2011]

Wolters, Klaus.
Handbuch der Klavierliteratur zu zwei Händen.
Zurich et Mayence: Atlantis Musikbuch Verlag, 2001

Spielhinweise

Eine der interessanten Herausforderungen beim Spielen klassischer Musik ist der Unterschied zwischen dem Pianoforte des späten 18. Jahrhunderts und dem heutigen Klavier. Die Unterschiede sind zwar groß, doch können wir mit unseren Kenntnissen über die damaligen Instrumente die Musik bereichern, auch wenn wir sie auf modernen Instrumenten spielen. So hatte das Klavier der Klassik leichtere (und weniger) Tasten, die Saiten verliefen parallel zueinander, d. h. es gab keine kreuzsaitige Bespannung, die Hämmer waren nicht mit Filz, sondern mit Leder bezogen, es war insgesamt zierlicher, hatte keinen Metallrahmen und eine andere Mechanik. All das bedeutet, dass wir den Klang, den Haydn oder Mozart hörten, nicht reproduzieren können. Wir können das moderne Klavier jedoch so spielen, dass es diesen anderen musikalischen Gegebenheiten gerecht wird. Um dies zu erreichen, sollte man mit starken dynamischen Kontrasten zwischen *forte* und *piano* arbeiten und das rechte Pedal so einsetzen, dass es nur bestimmte Stellen der Musik hervorhebt und nicht allgegenwärtig ist. Die Klangqualität sollte sich grundsätzlich eher auf die hohen Töne und nicht auf die Basstöne des Instruments konzentrieren. Letztendlich bildet das Konzept der historisch geprägten Spielpraxis (d. h. ein Verständnis dafür, wie Musik in einer anderen Epoche gespielt wurde und wie dies das eigene Spiel beeinflusst) eine hervorragende Grundlage für das Experimentieren mit Musik sowie für die Fähigkeit zuzuhören, zu bewerten und musikalische Entscheidungen zu treffen.

Carl Czerny (1791–1857)
1. Etude op. 161 Nr. 8
(♩ = 116)
Diese Etüde ist eine an effektive Übung zum Synchronspiel der Finger und enthält eine Folge verschiedener Handhaltungen. Damit beide Hände gut koordiniert werden können, sind präzise Bewegungen aus den Fingergelenken erforderlich. In Takt 3 und 4 werden die beiden Melodien aus Viertelnoten betont, die in den Sechzehnteln enthalten sind:

Das Konzept, eine Melodie mit Fingerübungen zu kombinieren, wird auch in der Kadenz in Takt 8-11 deutlich, die mit der rechten Hand gespielt wird.
Am besten setzt man sich die ersten Noten von Takt 11 als Zielpunkte. Dieser Moment der Betonung ist musikalisch bedeutsam und technisch von Vorteil, da er dem Spieler einen Moment Pause gönnt, in der er die linke Hand auf der zweiten Sechzehntel des Taktes platzieren kann.

Tommaso Giordani (ca. 1730–1806)
2. Keyboard Lesson No. 12, aus *12 Keyboard Lessons*
(♩ = 112)
Der Untertitel *Lesson No. 12* (Lektion Nr. 12) ist etwas irreführend. Der Begriff *Lektion* sollte nicht wörtlich genommen werden. Er bedeutet eher Schritt bzw. *Übungseinheit 12,* d. h. er bezeichnet nicht die Noten, die in der zwölften Lektion gespielt werden, sondern die Fähigkeiten, die der Komponist von den Schülern in ihren verschiedenen Entwicklungsstufen erwartet.
In Bezug auf die Stimmung erinnert das Stück an den frühen Haydn, und auch das Konzept, ungewöhnliche Modulationen einfließen zu lassen, ist zumindest tendenziell recht typisch für Haydn. Dennoch wird beim Hören des Stückes klar, dass Giordanis Stil sehr eigenständig ist. Es ist ausgesprochen einfallsreich, wenn nicht sogar für die damalige Zeit etwas gewagt, die zweite Hälfte des Werks (Takt 31) in e-Moll zu beginnen, nur um zwei Takte später bei Fis-Dur anzukommen.
Die größten Herausforderungen des Stückes bestehen darin, permanent ein gutes Gleichgewicht zwischen der rechten und linken Hand herzustellen, vor allem wenn die Hände über Kreuz spielen, sowie die Verzierungen stilistisch stimmig zu spielen. Giordani selbst schlug folgende Trillerspielweise vor (siehe **Anhang S. 66.**)

Prinz Louis Ferdinand von Preußen (1772–1806)
3. Fugue op. 7
(♩ = 72)
Diese *Fuge* nimmt im Werk des Komponisten eine ungewöhnliche Stellung ein. Sie ist sein einziges veröffentlichtes Klavierwerk, was für einen Pianisten, der für sein Improvisationstalent bekannt ist, eher untypisch ist. Auch ist eine Fuge als eher traditionelle Komposition für einen Komponisten ungewöhnlich, der ansonsten eher Kammermusikstücke in Sonaten- und Rondoform für verschiedene Ensembles komponierte.
Die vorliegende vierstimmige Fuge enthält einige dramatische, wenn nicht sogar unkonventionelle Momente. Die starken dynamischen Kontraste in Takt 17 weisen auf ein Stück hin, das sich hervorragend als Spielstück und nicht nur zu Übungszwecken eignet. Es ist ein faszinierendes Werk, das die Klangfülle des Klaviers voll zur Geltung bringt. Das Legato-Spiel ist ein wesentliches Merkmal des Stückes. Hierbei sollten die punktierten Halben beachtet werden, die gehalten werden müssen, um vor allem den Klang der Bassstimme voll zur Geltung zu bringen (Takt 28ff).

Friedrich Kalkbrenner (1785–1849)
4. Etude op. 20 Nr. 3
(♩. = ca. 66 – Angabe des Komponisten)
In Kalkbrenners *Etude* geht es darum, ein Gleichgewicht zwischen drei Stimmen herzustellen: Melodie, Bass und einer Mittelstimme, die durch ihren unaufdringlichen, wogenden Klang zwar ergänzt und unterstützt, aber nicht dominant ist. Die Melodie sollte ausdrucksvoll gespielt werden, indem hin und wieder der Einsatz der Sechzehntel verzögert wird. Das bewirkt, dass die Melodie gut zur Geltung kommt und die Musik schön fließt. Der Schluss der Etüde in Cis-Dur bildet (in der Erstausgabe) die Überleitung zu einem Stück in dieser Tonart, was den Tonartwechsel erklärt.

Joseph Haydn (1732– 1809)
5. Adagio, Hob. XV: 22/2
(♩ = 72)
Haydns *Adagio* ist ein relativ spätes Stück des Komponisten und stammt aus dem Jahr 1794. Die Faszination des Stückes liegt hauptsächlich in der Klangtransparenz der Stimmen. Daher sollte auch schon im Anfangstakt ein deutlicher Unterschied zwischen den gehaltenen Basstönen (Viertel) und den Triolen der Tenorstimme zu hören sein. Damit das Über-Kreuz-Spiel zu Beginn von Takt 19 nicht gehetzt klingt, sollte man sich Zeit lassen und nicht

versuchen, das hohe D in der rechten Hand zu früh zu spielen. Der Lauf in der rechten Hand in Takt 23 sollte sorgfältig gespielt werden, damit die elf Noten gleichmäßig über die drei Noten in der linken Hand verteilt werden. In Takt 29 sollten die Oktaven den Legato-Klang in der rechten Hand fortsetzen, was einen überlegten Einsatz des Pedals erfordert. In Takt 45 ist ein stummer Fingerwechsel in linken Hand erforderlich, um den angegebenen Fingersatz zu spielen.

Jan Ladislav Dusík (1760–1812)
6. Alla tedesca, Craw 145
(♩. = 80)

Dusíks *Alla tedesca* ist ein ausgezeichnetes Stück, bei dem man anhand eines praktischen Beispiels etwas über die Rondoform lernen kann. Der Komponist stellt in den verschiedenen Teilen des Stückes eine Reihe von Spieltechniken vor, die in zahlreichen klassischen Stücken zu finden sind. Das ist jedoch nicht als Kritik gemeint. Vielmehr können die Spieler anhand der neuen Satztechnik in Takt 17 und 38 eine ganze Reihe von klassischen Spieltechniken ausprobieren, und zwar alle innerhalb eines einzigen Werks. Teil A des Rondos kehrt in Takt 48 und 94 wieder, und der Moll-Teil, der wie ein Mittelteil aus dem Lehrbuch wirkt, verleiht dem Werk eine besondere Würze. In Takt 64–90 müssen beide Hände gut koordiniert werden, doch lässt sich das Stück gut spielen, so dass die technischen Anforderungen nicht so hoch sind wie man vielleicht zunächst annehmen könnte. In der Kadenz auf der letzten Seite sollten gefühlte zwei Schläge pro Takt beibehalten werden, damit die Rückkehr zum A-Teil einen nahtlosen Übergang bilden kann.

Johann Christian Bach (1735–1782)
7. Prestissimo, aus der Sonate op. 17 Nr. 2
(♩. = 132)

Bachs *Sonate in c-Moll* ist ein dreisätziges Werk, dessen Finale das hier vorliegende *Prestissimo* bildet. Die Tempoangabe „So schnell wie möglich" sollte vielleicht etwas näher erläutert werden. Es ist verlockend, sie auf das Grundtempo des Stückes anzuwenden und dadurch die Wahrnehmung des Tempos von der Stimme der linken Hand aus zu lenken. Bach verwendet in diesem Stück jedoch ohnehin schon einen lebhaft klingenden und größtenteils stetigen Achtelfluss, der erheblich dazu beiträgt, dass das Stück wirkt, als würde es schnell gespielt. Mit anderen Worten, wenn die Achtel in der linken Hand gut herausgearbeitet werden, muss das zugrunde liegende Tempo nicht zu schnell sein, damit das Stück *prestissimo* klingt. Ein weiterer Hinweis auf ein angemessenes Tempo ist der Triller in der rechten Hand in Takt 11. Um ihn gut zu spielen, braucht man etwas Zeit, damit die Noten klingen. Vielen Sequenzen im Stück, z. B. in Takt 1–10, liegen Dreiklänge zugrunde, und es ist hilfreich, das Stück mit vier Akkorden pro Takt zu üben, wann immer es möglich ist. Auf diese Weise kann sich die Akkordfolge in der linken Hand festigen. Darüber hinaus hilft es, das Stück auswendig zu lernen. In Takt 23–30 sollte die erste Note jeder Dreiergruppe deutlich betont werden, damit die rhythmische Präzision und der harmonische Fluss des Stückes aufrechterhalten werden.

Maria Szymanowska (1789–1831)
8. Etude in E
(♩ = 108)

Maria Szymanowskas *Etüde in E-Dur* ist eine raffiniert komponierte

Übung, in deren Verlauf ein Motiv weiterentwickelt und erweitert wird. Die Entwicklung des Motivs erfolgt größtenteils durch die Modulation nach verschiedenen Tonarten, z. B. ab Takt 35 nach F-Dur. Die Erweiterung erfolgt durch zunehmend anspruchsvolle Satztechniken innerhalb der Stimmen. Dies wird ab Takt 55 deutlich, wenn sich die rechte Hand zwischen zwei Oktaven bewegt – ein kompositorisches Mittel, das dem Stück noch mehr Ausdruckskraft verleiht. Diese Technik erfordert eine sorgfältige Vorbereitung, vor allem in der rechten Hand, die spielbereit und an der richtigen Stelle sein muss, bevor sie gefordert ist. Die Passage sollte langsam gespielt und die Bewegung der rechten Hand mit der linken Hand koordiniert werden. Auf diese Weise kann die rechte Hand recht schnell an die richtige Stelle gebracht werden.

Franz Schubert (1797–1828)
9. Adagio D.178
(♩ = 66)

Schuberts *Adagio D.178* ist ein eigenständiges Charakterstück, das von einem 17-jährigen Komponisten geschrieben wurde. Die abwechslungsreichen Satztechniken verleihen dem Werk eine improvisatorische Note, vor allem ab Takt 45. Das Grundtempo am Anfang des Stückes sollte dieser Abwechslung Rechnung tragen. Ab Takt 32 sollten die Ober- und Bassstimme ganz deutlich gespielt werden, damit die Dreischichtigkeit der Musik zur Geltung kommt. Die Achtelstimme sollte ziemlich leise mit dem Daumen gespielt werden, damit sie die Transparenz der Oberstimme nicht beeinträchtigt. Die Takte 55–57 und 68 werden zwar frei gespielt, doch sollten die notierten Notenwerte berücksichtigt werden. Übt man diese Passagen exakt im Takt, so kann man sie anschließend freier spielen und trotzdem ihren rhythmischen Rahmen beachten. Der dynamische Kontrast in Takt 65–70 sollte deutlich hervorgehoben werden, da hier verschiedene Stimmen im Spiel zu sein scheinen. Die *ff*-Stellen müssen auf jeden Fall dramatische Einwürfe sein, die die ansonsten ruhige Musik bedrohen.

Ludwig van Beethoven (1770–1827)
10. Allegretto WoO 53
(♩. = 76)

Beethovens *Allegretto WoO53* war ursprünglich als Satz der Klaviersonate op. 10 Nr. 1 gedacht, wurde von Beethoven jedoch vor der Veröffentlichung herausgenommen. Das Allegretto existiert in zwei Versionen, von denen die hier vorliegende die zweite ist. Die Verbindung zur Sonate op. 10 Nr. 1 ist jedoch wichtig, da es für das Verständnis von Stil und Stimmung des vorliegenden Stückes nützlich ist, sich die Sonate anzuhören. Die Achtelpassage in Takt 30–39 bereitet man am besten in Vierteln vor, jedoch mit dem in der Achtelpassage angegebenen Fingersatz. Dies fördert das harmonische Verständnis der Passage und trägt dazu bei, dass immer klar ist, wo die Finger als Nächstes platziert werden müssen.

Das *Maggiore* sieht zwar ganz leicht aus, doch muss jede Hand gut vorbereitet sein. Schließlich sollen die Noten ruhig und gleichmäßig klingen, um einen wirkungsvollen Kontrast zu den lebhaften anderen Teilen des Werkes zu bilden. Die Takte 40ff. können auf beide Hände verteilt werden, wie im Fingersatz des Herausgebers angegeben.

Wolfgang Amadeus Mozart (1756–1791)

11. Adagio KV 540
($\bullet$ = 42)

Mozarts *Adagio h-Moll* ist ein eigenständiges Werk, das vom Komponisten „Wien, 1788" datiert ist. Ob es als langsamer Satz für eine größer angelegte Klavierkomposition gedacht war, ist nicht bekannt. Allerdings führt der Komponist es in seinem eigenen Werkverzeichnis als Einzelstück auf, was darauf hindeutet, dass er es vermutlich nicht durch andere Stücke ergänzen wollte. Bei eingehender Betrachtung entpuppt sich das Adagio als ein sehr schön gestaltetes und musikalisch ausgesprochen abwechslungsreiches Werk. Man vergleiche nur die Art und Weise, wie Takt 1–6 und 15–21 geschrieben sind. Die Rückkehr des Hauptthemas, jedoch in einer anderen Lage, trägt zu einem abwechslungsreichen Timbre des Stückes bei. Die typischen plötzlichen dynamischen Kontraste im Stück sollten deutlich artikuliert werden, ohne abrupt zu klingen. Schließlich war das Pianoforte (das „Laut-leise"-Tasteninstrument) immer noch ein relativ neues Instrument, das gerade erst das Cembalo als wichtigstes Tasteninstrument der damaligen Zeit ablöste. Ein weiterer wichtiger Aspekt des Stückes ist die sorgfältige Konzeption der Stimmen, die immer gut zur Geltung kommen sollte.

In den Takten 32 und 34 sollte der punktierte Rhythmus durchgehend deutlich artikuliert werden, damit die Musik durch diese Figuration in Bewegung bleibt.

Václav Jan Tomášek (1774–1850)

12. Eclogue op. 66 Nr. 3
($\bullet$ = 76)

Das Schlussstück dieser Anthologie, Tomášeks *Eclogue*, ist ein hervorragendes Spielstück, das die Gelegenheit bietet, an der Drehung des Handgelenks zu arbeiten. Damit das Stück beim Vorspielen mühelos klingt (und sich ebenso anfühlt), sollte der stetige Sechzehntelfluss durch eine leichte Seitwärtsdrehung erzeugt werden, bei der der zweite Finger als Stütze fungiert. Mit anderen Worten, das Verhältnis zwischen der etwas lauteren Melodie und den leisen Sechzehnteln in der Begleitung wird durch die Fingergelenke erzeugt, die von dem beweglichen, leicht seitwärts gedrehten Handgelenk unterstützt werden. Das Trio erfordert kaum Pedaleinsatz, so dass der Kontrast zwischen den gehaltenen Akkorden in der rechten Hand und den kürzeren, arpeggierten Akkorden der linken Hand stärker zur Geltung kommt. Wenn das Stück ab dem Anfang wiederholt wird, kann man die Rückkehr des Hauptthemas variieren, indem man allmählich das Tempo wieder aufnimmt, anstatt wieder im Ausgangstempo zu beginnen.

Biografische Anmerkungen

Johann Christian Bach (1735–1782)

Johann Christian Bach war Johann Sebastian Bachs jüngster Sohn. Nachdem er zunächst von seinem Vater Musikunterricht erhalten hatte, ließ sich Johann Christian Bach von seinem älteren Bruder Carl Philip Emmanuel in Berlin weiter ausbilden. Anschließend ging er nach Italien und wurde 1760 Organist am Mailänder Dom. Nachdem er dort Kirchenmusik und Opern geschrieben hatte, zog er 1762 nach London, wo er Komponist am King's Theatre wurde. Hier stieg er zu einem ausgesprochen erfolgreichen Mitglied der Gesellschaft auf und wurde zweimal von Gainsborough porträtiert. Den größten Erfolg hatte Bach jedoch in seiner Eigenschaft als Veranstalter einer hoch angesehenen Konzertreihe, die er zusammen mit C. F. Abel organisierte. 1764 lernte Bach in London den jungen Mozart kennen, und beide Komponisten hatten zeit ihres Lebens ein Faible für die Werke des jeweils anderen. Johann Christian Bachs Klavierkompositionen sind ein sehr interessantes Beispiel für die Einbeziehung des (damals) relativ neu entwickelten Pianofortes, für das er in einem eleganten, frühklassischen Stil schrieb. Seine Klaviersonaten op. 5 (1766) und op. 17 (1773/74) wurden in Paris, Wien, Amsterdam und London veröffentlicht – ein deutlicher Hinweis auf die Popularität des Komponisten. Außerdem schrieb er zusammen mit Pasquale Ricci eine hervorragend aufgebaute Klavierschule (1786), mit der die Schüler die einzelnen Spieltechniken der Reihe nach lernen können.

Ludwig van Beethoven (1770–1827)

Beethovens Einfluss auf die musikalische Richtung seiner Zeit sowie auf die musikalische Entwicklung nachfolgender Komponisten war beträchtlich und vielschichtig. Seine eigene stilistische Entwicklung als Komponist lässt sich in drei verschiedene Zeitabschnitte einteilen: bis ca. 1802 (erste Schaffensperiode), von 1802 bis 1812 (zweite Schaffensperiode) und ab 1812 (dritte Schaffensperiode). Hinsichtlich Beethovens Klavierkompositionen reflektieren diese Perioden das klassische Erbe seiner Anfangsphase, die Entwicklung seines virtuosen Spielstils und die darauf folgende Individualität seiner späteren Werke in Bezug auf Technik und Aufbau.

Als Komponist zeichnete sich Beethoven in fast allen Formen der Instrumentalmusik aus, von Streichquartetten über Klaviersonaten und Konzerte bis zu Sinfonien. Die Spontaneität, Stärke und emotionale Wirkung seiner Musik waren jedoch das Ergebnis eines akribisch gestalteten Kompositionsprozesses, den er in seinen Skizzenbüchern und Autographen dokumentierte. Beethoven war ein erfolgreicher Pianist, obgleich seine Leistung in zeitgenössischen Berichten je nach Perspektive des Autors unterschiedlich bewertet wurde. Während einige Beethovens kraftvollen Klang lobten, fanden andere sein Spiel chaotisch und unkontrolliert. Die meisten Quellen sind sich jedoch über die Wirkung einig, die Beethoven mit seinem Spiel auf sein Publikum ausübte.

Ein Klavierwerk, das beide Sichtweisen seines Spiels vereint, ist die Fantasie für Klavier op. 77, ein Werk, das weithin als niedergeschriebene Version einer Improvisation angesehen wird. Es enthält viele für Beethoven typische Aspekte hinsichtlich Harmonik, Melodie und Aufbau und bietet daher einen einzigartigen Einblick in das Schaffen des großen Musikers.

Beethovens kompositorische Leistungen waren so beachtlich, dass nachfolgende Komponistengenerationen von Schubert bis Schumann, Liszt und Brahms einige Zeit zögerten, bevor sie in einem Genre komponierten, das Beethoven sich zuvor zu eigen gemacht hatte.

Carl Czerny (1791–1857)

Czerny hat maßgeblich zur Entwicklung des Klavierspiels beigetragen. Obwohl er hauptsächlich als Beethovens Schüler und Liszts Lehrer bekannt ist, war Czerny ein interessanter eigenständiger Komponist. Die Systematik, mit der er seine eigenen Sammlungen mit Klavierübungen zusammenstellte, entsprach seiner Art, seinen Unterricht bei Beethoven und seine frühen Eindrücke von Liszt gewissenhaft aufzuzeichnen. Kein Wunder, dass er hauptsächlich in diesem Zusammenhang Erwähnung findet.

Czernys Fähigkeiten als Komponist kommen wahrscheinlich am besten in zweien seiner frühen Werke zum Ausdruck: der Klaviersonate op. 7 (1830 von Liszt in Paris gespielt) und seiner hochdramatischen Sinfonie in c-Moll. Mit 16 Jahren entschied sich Czerny gegen eine Laufbahn als Pianist und für den Lehrerberuf. Als Lehrer arbeitete er häufig zehn Stunden und mehr am Tag, bis er sich 1836 zur Ruhe setzte.

Czerny hinterließ das wohl umfassendste Unterrichtsrepertoire aller Klavierlehrer seiner Zeit, wie an seiner *Pianoforte-Schule* op. 500, einem Werk, das er 1846 aktualisierte, zu sehen ist.

Jan Ladislav Dusík (1760–1812)

Dusík wurde in eine Familie aus Berufsmusikern hineingeboren. Sein Vater war Organist und Komponist und seine Mutter spielte Harfe, ein Instrument, für das er später komponierte. Seine Ausbildung erhielt er zunächst an einer Jesuitenschule, dann besuchte er ein Prager Gymnasium und anschließend die Prager Universität. Es folgte eine Zeit verschiedener Anstellungen, Konzertreisen und Studien in ganz Europa – von Belgien (1779) bis Hamburg, St. Petersburg und Litauen. 1786 kam Dusík nach Paris. Hier wurde Marie Antoinette seine Mäzenin, bevor seine Reiselust ihn 1788 erneut nach Mailand führte. Nach einer kurzen Rückkehr nach Paris kurz vor der Revolution ließ er sich 1789 in London nieder. Hier blieb er zehn Jahre, lehrte Komposition und gab Konzerte. Dusíks Anstellung bei und Freundschaft mit Prinz Louis Ferdinand von Preußen trugen zur Entstehung eines seiner bekanntesten Klavierwerke bei, der Sonate in fis-Moll, op. 61, die er 1806 in Gedenken an den Prinzen komponierte.

Dusík's Vorliebe für Musik mit programmatischen Zügen beeinflusste zwar die frühromantischen Komponisten, war jedoch nicht seine einzige Leistung. Ein Vergleich zwischen Dusíks Werken und der Musik von einigen seiner (später) bekannteren Zeitgenossen belegt die Qualität von Dusíks motivischem und harmonischem Erfindungsreichtum.

Tommaso Giordani (ca. 1730–1806)

Giordani war ein italienischer Komponist, der einen Großteil seines Erwachsenenlebens in London und Dublin verbrachte. Es sind nur wenige Einzelheiten über seine frühe musikalische Entwicklung bekannt, doch gibt es Aufzeichnungen über eine von ihm komponierte Oper, *La commediante fatta cantatrice*, die 1756 in Covent Garden aufgeführt wurde. 1764 zog er nach Dublin und kehrte einige Jahr später als Komponist und Kapellmeister am King's Theatre nach London zurück. 1783 ging er wieder nach Dublin, wo er 1806 starb. Wie viele Musiker jener Zeit ging auch Giordani einer Reihe musikalischer Aktivitäten nach: Er komponierte, dirigierte, unterrichtete und veranstaltete Konzerte. Dieser unternehmerische Aspekt machte einen guten Teil seines Einkommens aus. Unter seinen Schülern befand sich auch John Field (1782–1837), dessen Nocturnes für Klavier einen nachhaltigen Einfluss auf die Klaviermusik des 19. Jahrhunderts hatten.

Joseph Haydn (1732–1809)

Die Bewertung von Haydns Stellung als Komponist hat sich im Laufe der Zeit immer wieder verändert. Zahlreiche Berichte konzentrieren sich auf die Sicherheit und Stabilität seiner fast 30-jährigen Anstellung bei der Familie Esterhazy in Eisenstadt bei Wien. Trotz dieses verhältnismäßig beständigen Lebens (zumindest im Vergleich zu vielen seiner Zeitgenossen, nicht zuletzt Mozart) wurde Haydns Musik ab 1780 veröffentlicht und erfreute sich zunehmender Beliebtheit, was dem Komponisten wachsende nationale und internationale Bedeutung einbrachte.

Seine Besuche in London ab 1791 untermauerten seine musikalischen und wirtschaftlichen Erfolge. Seine frühen Jahre sahen jedoch völlig anders aus. Nach seiner Ausbildung als Chorsänger und Violinist hielt sich Haydn, der kein virtuoser Musiker war, mit Unterricht und als Mitglied wechselnder Ensembles, die bei Veranstaltungen musizierten, über Wasser. Als Komponist eignete sich Haydn als Autodidakt nur langsam die notwendigen Fähigkeiten an. Ab Mitte der 1760er-Jahre entwickelter dann allmählich seinen eigenen Musikstil.

Haydns Klavierwerke umfassen 60 Sonaten, Einzelstücke und Variationen. Obwohl er kein Klaviervirtuose war, wusste er genau, worauf es bei einer Komposition für das Pianoforte ankam. All seine Werke lassen sich sehr gut spielen (ungeachtet ihrer verschiedenen Schwierigkeitsgrade), doch ist das Überraschungsmoment, das sich sowohl in der Harmonik als auch im Aufbau ausdrücken kann, letztendlich für den besonderen Charme vieler Stücke verantwortlich. Haydns Klavierkompositionen sind niemals starr und daher immer unvorhersehbar.

Friedrich Kalkbrenner (1785–1849)

Kalkbrenner galt zu Lebzeiten als einer der führenden Pianisten seiner Zeit. In den 1820er-Jahren teilten sich Johann Nepomuk Hummel und Kalkbrenner das Renommee, die besten Interpreten auf dem Pianoforte zu sein. Nach der Ausbildung durch seinen Vater ging Kalkbrenner aufs Pariser Konservatorium, bevor er ab 1803 in Wien weiterstudierte. Nach einiger Zeit als Konzertpianist lebte er von 1814 bis 1823 in London. Dort arbeitete er als gefragter Klavierlehrer und vermarktete einen so genannten Handbildner, ein Gerät (das ursprünglich von Johann Logier stammte), das Anfängern eine gute Handhaltung für das Klavierspiel ermöglichen sollte. 1825 kehrte Kalkbrenner als wohlhabender und hoch angesehener Pianist nach Paris zurück.

Seine Kompositionen beschränken sich hauptsächlich auf das Klavier und bestehen aus vielen verschiedenen Werken von Sonaten bis zu kleineren Etüden, die er zur Entwicklung einer guten Klaviertechnik schrieb.

Wolfgang Amadeus Mozart (1756–1791)

Mozart wurde in eine äußerst musikalische Familie hineingeboren. Sein Vater Leopold war Orchesterviolinist und Lehrer in Salzburg, und seine ältere Schwester Nannerl hatte bereits ihre Fähigkeiten als Pianistin unter Beweis gestellt. Mozart machte im Musikunterricht rasche Fortschritte – so rasch, dass sein Vater ihn zu einer Konzertreise durch Deutschland und anschließend nach London und Paris mitnahm, die dreieinhalb Jahre dauerte. Danach ließ sich Mozart 1766 in Salzburg nieder. Von 1769–1772 folgten alljährliche Reisen nach Italien, auf denen Mozart – wie in seinem gesamten Leben – Kontakt zu vielen anderen Musikern knüpfte. Anfang der 1780er-Jahre schien Mozart sich in ein Leben als freischaffender Musiker in all seiner Vielfalt eingefunden zu haben. Einige seiner erfolgreichsten Klavierkonzerte stammen aus dieser Zeit, ebenso viele Streichquartette, von denen er einige an der Seite ihres Widmungsträgers, Joseph Haydn, spielte. Am Ende des Jahrzehnts (und zu Beginn des nächsten) feierte Mozart mit Werken wie *Cosi fan tutte* und *Die Zauberflöte* große Erfolge als Opernkomponist.

Die verschiedenen Lebensabschnitte des Komponisten spiegeln sich in der Vielseitigkeit seiner Klavierkompositionen wider. Einige seiner frühesten Werke entstanden, als Mozart erst fünf Jahre alt war, eine Zeit, in der er hauptsächlich kürzere Tänze schrieb. Zu seinen Werken als Erwachsener zählen Sonaten, Variationen und Einzelstücke – viele davon waren für den Eigengebrauch geschrieben.

Prinz Louis Ferdinand von Preußen (1772–1806)
Prinz Louis Ferdinand von Preußen war der Neffe König Friedrichs des Großen (1712–1786). Er war Berufssoldat und starb 1806 im Gefecht von Saalfeld im Kampf gegen die französischen Truppen Napoleons.

Musik war ein wichtiger Bestandteil von Louis Ferdinands Erziehung (Friedrich der Große war ein hervorragender Flötist), so dass sein musikalisches Erbe auf vielen verschiedenen Ebenen dokumentiert ist. Erstens gibt es Musikstücke, die dem Prinzen gewidmet sind, darunter Beethovens Klavierkonzert op. 37. Zweitens komponierte er selbst Werke, vor allem Kammermusik, die von seinen Zeitgenossen und nachfolgenden Generationen hoch gelobt wurden. So spielte beispielsweise Schumann die vom Prinzen komponierte Kammermusik für Klavier, und Liszt schrieb ein Werk, das ein Thema von Louis Ferdinand als Vorlage hatte. Und drittens konnte Louis Ferdinand so gut improvisieren, dass es Berichte über musikalische Zusammenkünfte in Salons gibt, bei denen Louis Ferdinand und Jan Ladislav Dussek auf zwei Klavieren improvisierten. Die Fuge in g-Moll in dieser Anthologie (op. 7) ist das einzige Werk des Prinzen für Soloklavier. Die meisten anderen Werke wurden für Kammermusikensembles geschrieben.

Franz Schubert (1797–1828)
Schuberts wurde zunächst von seinem Vater und seinen Brüdern unterrichtet, die ihm Klavier, Violine und Viola beibrachten. Im Alter von elf Jahren erhielt er ein Chorstipendium, das ihm eine Ausbildung bei Salieri ermöglichte. Mit 16 Jahren entschied sich Schubert für eine Ausbildung als Lehrer und begann ein Jahr später, in der Schule seines Vaters zu arbeiten. Mit 17 schrieb er bereits einige seiner frühen Meisterwerke für Klavier und Gesang, den *Erlkönig* und *Gretchen am Spinnrade*. 1816 gab Schubert seinen Lehrerposten auf und ging nach Wien, wo er im Stadtzentrum lebte und sich auf das Komponieren konzentrierte. Eine Zeit der finanziellen Unsicherheit folgte, bis er Ende 1819 sein erstes größeres Kammermusikstück, das *Forellenquintett*, schrieb. Im Frühjahr 1821 führte der Erfolg des *Erlkönigs* zur Veröffentlichung seiner Lieder durch Diabelli, was ihm eine kurze Zeit der finanziellen Sicherheit einbrachte. Von 1820–23 beschäftigte er sich vorwiegend mit der Komposition von Opernmusik, einem nicht besonders erfolgreichen Unterfangen. In seinen drei letzten Lebensjahren widmete er sich der Komposition von Kammermusik und sinfonischen Werken.

Mit wenigen Ausnahmen legte Schubert in seinen Klavierkompositionen nicht so viel Wert auf die äußerlichen technischen Aspekte, die einige seiner Zeitgenossen anwandten. Stattdessen liegen die Herausforderungen seiner Stücke immer in der Musik selbst und dem Bevorzugen von musikalischer Aussage über rein technischer Darstellung.

Maria Szymanowska (1789– 1831)
Szymanowska war eine der berühmtesten Pianistinnen ihrer Zeit. Sie wurde in Warschau geboren und unternahm ab ca. 1815 eine Tournee durch ganz Europa, wo sie von Musikern und Schriftstellern, u. a. Johann Wolfgang von Goethe, hoch gelobt wurde. Ab Ende der 1820er Jahre lebte sie in St. Petersburg, wo ihr Salon große gesellschaftliche und künstlerische Beachtung fand. Als Komponistin schrieb Szymanowska Klavierstücke, die den Geschmack der damaligen Zeit widerspiegelten, u. a. Polonaisen, Walzer, Mazurkas, Nocturnes, Etüden und Charakterstücke. Viele dieser Werke lassen ein hervorragendes klaviertechnisches Verständnis erkennen und sind Beispiele für Kompositionen, die auf das Instrument zugeschnitten sind.

In ihrem privaten Musikalbum werden ihre musikalischen Verbindungen deutlich: Es enthält Beiträge von Beethoven, Moscheles, Ogiński und vielen anderen (siehe Classical Piano Anthology Volume 3, ED 13440).

Václav Jan Tomášek (1774–1850)
Tomášek wurde 1774 in Skutsch (Böhmen) geboren. Nach anfänglichen Geigen- und Gesangsstunden erlernte er das Orgelspiel. Tomášeks Interessen waren breit gefächert, wie seine Jura-, Mathematik- und Ästhetikstudien zeigen. Obwohl er Kontakt zu dem Komponisten Kozeluh hatte, erwarb sich Tomášek sein musikalisches Wissen anscheinend größtenteils durch das Studium von Abhandlungen über das Komponieren, u. a. Werke von Mattheson, Marpurg und Jirnberger. 1806 wurde Tomášek Musiklehrer der Familie des Grafen Buquoy in Prag. Ab 1820 lebte er als hoch angesehener unabhängiger Komponist und Lehrer in Prag, wo er in der musikalischen Elite der Stadt eine zentrale Stellung einnahm. Tomášek war mit Haydn und Beethoven befreundet und hinterließ als Lehrer ein bedeutendes Erbe. Zu seinen Schülern zählten der Pianist Alexander Dreyschock (1818–1869), der Musikkritiker Eduard Hanslick (1825–1904) sowie der Komponist Jan Václav Voříšek (1791–1825). Tomášeks größter Beitrag zum Klavierrepertoire waren die sieben Sammlungen mit *Eklogen*, überwiegend gefühlvollen Charakterstücken, die einige von Schuberts Klavierstücken sowie Elemente aus Mendelssohns *Lieder ohne Worte* vorwegnahmen.

Bibliografie

Hinson, Maurice.
Guide to the Pianist's Repertoire.
Bloomington und Indianapolis: Indiana University Press, 2000

MacGrath, Jane.
The Pianist's *Guide to Standard Teaching and Performance Literature.*
Van Nuys: Alfred Publishing Co., 1995

Prosnitz, Adolf.
Handbuch der Klavierliteratur.
Wien: Doblinger, 1908

Sadie, Stanley (ed.).
Grove Concise Dictionary of Music.
London: MacMillan Publishers, 1988

Sadie, Stanley (ed.)
Grove Dictionary of Music online.
[accessed 04/04/2011]

Wolters, Klaus.
Handbuch der Klavierliteratur zu zwei Händen.
Zürich und Mainz: Atlantis Musikbuch Verlag, 2001

Appendix / Annexe / Anhang

The following text and performance directions are taken verbatim from Tommaso Giordani's *12 Keyboard Lessons*, published by Longman & Broderip (London, 1780).

Explanation of the Graces in Music

which if carefully attended to, and properly applied, particularly in the Executive part, give that Brilliancy to the Performance which would otherwise appear Languid and void of those pleasing expressions which are naturally meant to convey an agreeable sensation to the mind of the Hearer as well as the Performer.

Also available from Schott Music

Franz Liszt
Album Leaves and Short Piano Pieces

Selection and Commentaries
by Nils Franke and Ateş Orga

ED 9054

This collection draws together leaves and fragments reflecting Liszt's ability to write simply yet highly effectively for the piano, making a central case for some of his lesser-known miniatures

The editors have placed an emphasis on a period (from the 1840s to the 1860s) during which Liszt consciously refined the effectiveness of his own piano writing, often through clarifying revisions of transcendentally difficult earlier material.

Including an introduction to each piece as well as a teaching and learning commentary

Contents:

CD Track List / Plages du CD / CD-Titelverzeichnis

No.	Title	Composer	Duration
1.	Etude Op. 161 No. 8	Carl Czerny	0:40
2.	Keyboard Lesson No. 12 *from* 12 Keyboard Lessons	Tommaso Giordani	5:25
3.	Fugue Op. 7	Prince Louis Ferdinand of Prussia	3:24
4.	Etude Op. 20 No. 3	Friedrich Kalkbrenner	5:12
5.	Adagio, Hob. XV: 22/2	Joseph Haydn	2:51
6.	Alla tedesca, Craw 145	Jan Ladislav Dusík	2:16
7.	Prestissimo *from* Sonata Op. 17 No. 2	Johan Christian Bach	5:52
8.	Etude in E	Maria Szymanowska	5:35
9.	Adagio D.178	Franz Schubert	2:00
10.	Allegretto WoO 53	Ludwig van Beethoven	6:16
11.	Adagio KV 540	Wolfgang Amadeus Mozart	12:49
12.	Eclogue Op. 66 No. 3	Václav Jan Tomášek	3:47
	Total duration		**55:27**